Somerset Coalmining Life

Cover illustration: a silent tribute to King George VI on the occasion of his funeral in 1952   (Dennis Rendell Collection)

Somerset Coalmining Life

Fred Flower

with illustrations by Alan Summers

Millstream Books

To the Somerset Miners

The publishers wish to acknowledge the help afforded by
Dennis Rendell in providing material for use in this book

First published 1990

Millstream Books
7 Orange Grove
Bath BA1 1LP

This book has been composed in
New Baskerville type by Ryburn Typesetting Ltd, Halifax
Printed in Great Britain by BPCC Wheatons Ltd, Exeter

© Fred Flower 1990

ISBN 0 948975 23 7

Contents

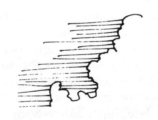

Foreword

In writing this book I hope to give readers an insight into the Somerset Coalfield, an indication of how the coalmines worked and of the life and times of the average miner and his family during the coalmining epoch. Literally speaking, I was born into coalmining for I was born in my grandfather's house next to the furnace shaft of the Greyfield Colliery in the parish of Clutton, where he was involved in the management of the pits, so it was not surprising that I became interested and indeed involved in coalmining at a very early age. I myself started work in the coalmines at the age of 14 but, unlike my grandfather, I was not destined to take part in management, though from his diaries I know that at least I share his interests.

As far as I am aware, little of any consequence has previously been recorded relating to the workings of the Somerset mines, and it would be an injustice to all our miners if some record of their work could not be made before it becomes too late, especially as Somerset coalminers are becoming fewer with every passing year. I have managed to cobble this book together largely from experience, old diaries and a wealth of information gathered from generations of older miners as I passed along life's way.

Although it has been a pleasure sifting through a lifetime of mining history, I must admit it has not been easy retracing all those steps down memory lane and, in addition, having to compete with my dear wife for the kitchen table. She, it seemed, always had cakes to make, ironing or sewing to do every time I wanted to get on with my typing, but it was a challenge.

I do not pretend to know every detail of what happened in every coalmine or what conditions were like at any given time, and I am aware that many improvisations had to be made in some mines in order to deal with many abnormal situations, but basically most of the work was the same throughout the coalfield.

Looking back, I think it was a privilege to have witnessed the wonders of the earth and the comradeship of the men who worked in it; the costs in human terms were very high but who knows, perhaps they were meant to be.

1. Early History

The coalfields of North Somerset formed a variable pattern of undulating coal seams, punctuated by many geological faults of various dimensions, over a fairly large area. They stretched from Pensford in the north, veering south-westerly around Bishop Sutton, Clutton and Farrington Gurney, and thence, traversing the Mendip foothills, to Mells. The eastern boundary ran roughly in a line north-east of Marksbury, Stanton Prior, Tunley and Dunkerton, thence to Peasedown and Shoscombe, and then, bearing southwards, around the extreme fringes of Radstock to link up with the Mells area, skirting the edge of Frome.

The coal seams were located in the strata known as Carboniferous. Coal was formed from vast masses of vegetable matter deposited from the luxuriant growth of plants many millions of years ago. Later marine incursions reduced vast areas of vegetation to decay in very swampy conditions.

The botanical origin of the vegetation cannot easily be defined; no doubt the swamps produced an abundance of mosses, reeds and many other species of succulent plants which thrive in wet conditions. Large ferns must have been flourishing at that time as fossils of their leaves were found in great profusion throughout the coalfield. Incidentally, some fish fossils were also found in at least one mine at Radstock.

It is not easy to assess the exact number of seams there were in the coalfield as the number of workable seams differed slightly in some areas from others, but a fair estimate might be put at six or seven, found in tiers at various depths, the thicknesses varying from 18 inches to two feet. Any seam thicker than this would be regarded as unusual.

THE SOMERSET COALFIELD

showing the principal mines and railways

Pensford •

Bromley •

MARKSBURY ■

Bishop • Sutton

Burchells •
■ CLUTTON

Greyfield •

Upper Conygre •
TIMSBURY ■
Lower Conygre •

Tunley

Dunkerton

Paulton Engine •

Radford •

Camerton •
PEASEDOWN ■

PAULTON ■

FARRINGTON GURNEY ■

Clandown •
Old Pit •
Middle Pit •
Ludlows •

Braysdown

■ RADSTOCK

Marsh Lane

Old Mills

Norton Hill •

Writhlington

Kilmersdon

STRATTON ON THE FOSSE ■

New Rock •

Chamborough •

Newbury •

Mells •

Moorewood •

Strap

Nettlebridge •

Vobster •

• Coalmine   ~~~ Somersetshire Coal Canal

■ Town or Village   +++++ Railway

9

At some stage during the evolution of the coalfield, it is almost certain that some volcanic action took place, most probably in the area of the Mendip Hills. It seems unlikely that the action lasted for any great length of time although some activity may still be taking place beneath the ground in that area and is the most likely source of the Bath Spa warm waters. There was some evidence of such action in at least one area of the Pensford Colliery, in No 3 seam, where the roof, just above the coal, resembled a bed of burnt rock. Incidentally the coal in this area also had a very dull and lifeless appearance.

When these coal seams were formed, some 50 million years ago, it is fairly obvious that the decaying vegetation beds in the lagoons and swamps were comparatively flat, but subsequent earthquakes and severe earth movements caused a great deal of distortion throughout the coalfield. When mining began, it was discovered that the seams ran obliquely to the surface, and in all areas they were bent into almost basin-like shapes. The coal formations were not fragmented to any great extent but the breaks in the rock formations quite often caused many serious problems.

The coals produced from these seams were of a bituminous nature but there was a slight variation in the mineral and chemical content of some coals in the different localities. The harder coals proved to be the best for all domestic purposes, while the softer ones were most suitable for industrial uses; the best coking coals were produced in the most southerly part of the coalfield, in the Mendip area, where the gas content was much higher.

As a result of the eruptions and earth movements, some of the top series coal seams were thrown up near the surface in the areas of Stratton-on-the-Fosse, Holcombe, Clutton and High Littleton; these were known as outcrop areas and this is where coalmining in Somerset first began.

A great deal of obscurity still exists regarding the early history of coalmining in Somerset, but it is believed by some historians that coal was being mined as far back as Roman times, although there is little evidence to substantiate this claim. It is, however, an established fact that they did mine lead on the Mendips.

The outcrop area in the southern part of the coalfield around Stratton-on-the-Fosse had very strong connections with the Roman occupation and if indeed they did discover coal, they may well have stumbled on it by accident while engaged in road making or excavating for lead. In any event, they could not have exploited their find to any great extent as the coal reserves were apparently still intact at a much later date.

During the 16th and 17th centuries, lead was extensively mined on the Mendips and was a very prosperous industry. During this time a large force of miners was employed and when the lead mines became exhausted, some of these miners could well have formed the nucleus for the coalmining industry, destined also to become very important.

Coalmining in Somerset began in a modest way. It is believed that coal was being mined at Stratton-on-the-Fosse as early as the 15th century. As one might expect, only very small amounts of coal were being produced in those early years and sales were confined, in the main, to the local populace. The start of this new industry did little to arouse the enthusiasm of the local population. Their main source of fuel was wood and at that time there was still a plentiful supply, so they were reluctant to turn to the new magic fuel of coal. Moreover they were very set in their ways, lived at a more leisurely pace and could not be easily tempted to change their habits. But as the population grew and wood became more and more scarce, the changeover to coal began to take place.

The first coals were dug, most probably, by the excavation method, but there was obviously a limit to the coal which could be raised in this way, as the coal seams sank deeper into the earth. The excavation method was followed by driving inclines or levels. This involved the miners following the seam into the ground, making a tunnel as they went, and expanding and developing small coalfaces on both sides of the tunnel. No doubt this method proved to be more productive but it also brought problems of drainage and ventilation. Nevertheless the method continued for many years. It might be interesting to note that history was repeated during the 1926 coal strike when miners from

High Littleton, Rotcombe and Mearns worked on an outcrop of coal on the Kingwell estate at Rotcombe, working in the very same way. Permission had been given by the late Captain Scobell, who was then in residence at Kingwell Hall which, as many will recall, was later destroyed by fire.

Most of these early mining ventures were of course only short-term enterprises, the policy being to extract as much coal as possible from them and then, as difficulties arose, to abandon them in favour of other sites. It is not known how many of these early mining excursions were carried out in this period, but it is known that there was a significant rise in coal output towards the middle of the 17th century, at the time when the leadmining industry was reaching its peak. The possibility that there may have been hundreds of small coal works dotted around the outcrops cannot be ruled out.

It was during the 17th century that the first of the vertical pit shafts were sunk. These were known locally as 'bell pits', deriving their name from their shape. The shafts were sunk in the outcrop areas to a depth of anything from 40 to 60 feet. They were normally about four feet square but towards the bottom they were made much wider all round, forming a bell shape; this was necessary to make room for manoeuvre and to develop the coalface. Incidentally, the bottom of these pits later became known as the 'coal hole'.

Nature was not very kind to the men who were destined to mine coal in Somerset; the seams were comparatively thin, geological faults were numerous, and the undulating coal formations made mining conditions very difficult and unpleasant to work in. It was probably the unique methods adopted to work these seams, and the way in which the miners adapted themselves to work in such bad conditions, which earned them the distinction of being some of the best miners in the world. We miners of the 20th century should ever be grateful to our early pioneers for the courage and skills which we inherited from them.

The workforce required to work these small mines consisted of about three or four men and a few small boys. The men worked at the coalface and their daily output was governed by the amount of coal the boys could manage to carry, in baskets, from the coalface to the pit bottom. This only amounted to a few tons per day.

Knowledge of coalmining at this time was very scarce and it must be assumed that any techniques adopted were gained by trial and error and from the miners' own daily experiences. The coal was hewn with a hand pick, and roof supports were cut from the nearest tree. A tallow candle provided but a flicker of light for the men working underground. Coal was brought to the surface by two men winding on a windlass with a fibre rope, very much like the winder used to draw water from a well, except that it had two handles, one on either side. The amount of coal hauled up at each winding was about one hundredweight, contained in a reed or wicker basket.It must be assumed that the men and boys who worked the mine were either lowered and raised by this rather hazardous method or else they could have climbed ladders attached to the walls of the shaft. Either way, with only a candle to light their path, was very unpleasant.

Although coalmining had hitherto been more or less confined to the Mendip area in the south, by the early part of the 17th century the industry was expanding and several coal works had been established at High Littleton and Clutton. Progress in the industry, however, was slow and the outlook for its future prosperity was very bleak for a long time.

It must be remembered that roads as we now know them were non-existent at the time, and the best one could hope for were very narrow, badly-surfaced or muddy tracks, some of which were privately owned. Rivers and streams could only be crossed at fords which proved formidable obstacles for horses and carts when in full flood. Add to this the hilly contours of the countryside and it is obvious that transportation was poor to say the least. In fact conditions were so bad in winter that pack-horses, mules and even donkeys were the only means of transport available for delivering coal to isolated villages. Some improvement, however, was being made by the end of the century and at last the industry was beginning to flourish.

The improvement in the industry was reflected in the fact that prospectors and landowners in many other areas were becoming more than interested in coalmining, and it was not surprising that more mines were being sunk. The initial success of the small mines at Clutton and High Littleton was followed by sinkings at Farrington, Paulton and the Midsomer Norton and Welton areas, but a good many of these early projects proved to be unsuccessful and it was not until much later that coalmining in these areas began to make its mark.

Towards the end of the century, mines in the Mendip areas were being sunk to much greater depths to reach the lower seams. By now the miners had become much more knowledgeable of the ground they worked in and no doubt many new techniques had been introduced and perfected as a result of lifetimes of experience. In spite of these, the deeper mines posed more problems and underground developments were still limited to the amount of coal which could be raised to the surface. Although coal production had improved encouragingly, output still remained relatively low. Deep mining presented two problems in particular, those of ventilation and drainage. Good ventilation was essential to ensure that gases were not allowed to accumulate in isolated pockets where they could easily be ignited with a naked light. Water was for ever prevalent in all mines and a constant problem, quite often being responsible for the closing of some mines for long periods. Those mines which were fortunate enough to be working on seams on high ground and above the valleys were in a position to drive an adit or tunnel down to the valley and drain the water out in this way. The less fortunate could only avail themselves of wind-powered pumps or water wheels, neither of which were very reliable.

There were probably seven or eight deep mines in production or about to become productive in the Mendip area at the end of the 17th century, a century which had proved to be one of frustration for the industry. There was an increased demand for coal particularly as small factories such as potteries, glass works, foundries, lime kilns, etc, in nearby towns, became more dependent on coal. This led to much fiercer competition but any increase in production had very little chance of reaching a wider market until transport facilities could be much improved.

As mines were sunk to much greater depths, their life expectancy increased considerably and the potential for increased production became evident. But as the problems of raising extra coal to the surface increased, obviously hand winding could no longer be expected to provide adequate haulage from the pit bottom. So, what may be described as one of the first mechanical aids ever to be used in the Somerset mines was introduced, the 'horse drum'. A horse, harnessed to a rope, was led round in a circle, winding the rope round a wooden drum until the receptacle carrying the coal reached the surface. The action was then reversed to return the empty to the pit bottom. A similar system. known as the 'horse gin', was introduced a little later for hauling along steep roadways underground. These systems were not improved upon and remained in operation for at least 70 or 80 years.

As the increased workforce, engaged to work in the deeper mines, developed more coalfaces and produced more coal, it became necessary to transport it more quickly to the pit bottom. The old method of carrying it in baskets was discontinued and the system of carting introduced. The carts, which later became better known as 'putts', were made of wood, about 3 feet long, 2 feet wide, and 9 inches deep. The wood was about 1½ inches thick and the bottom of the putt was fixed roughly 3 or 4 inches off the floor to prevent it dragging and help it to ride over the accumulated dust and rubble of the roadway. The sides were rounded, both front and rear, and a metal strip was attached to the edges to preserve the wood and to ensure as smooth a run as possible. Two end pieces were fitted where the curves began on the sides, and an iron loop or shackle fitted at each end, enabling it to be pulled along from either end without it having to be turned round. When completed the putt looked very much like a snow sledge. When fully laden it contained approximately one hundredweight of coal and was pulled along by a boy wearing a rope girdle round his waist, known as a 'guss'. The guss consisted of a length of rope which was fitted and measured around the waist, adding a little more to allow for splicing or, as it was better known, for tucking. Having determined the length of rope

15

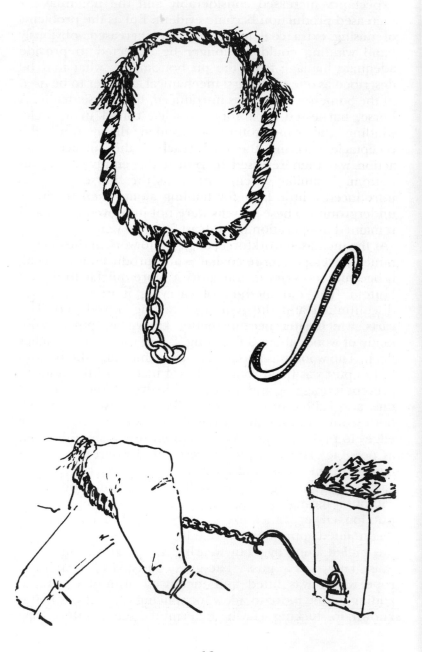

to be used, a piece of iron chain, consisting of a dozen links or so, was threaded onto it; the two ends were then spliced, or tucked, into each other and made to fit round the waist as comfortably as possible. A 'crook', about 8 inches long and made from a half-inch iron bar, normally by the colliery blacksmith, was hooked at each end to complete the harness.

To pull the putt, the chain was passed through the legs to the rear and the crook hitched on respectively to the shackle on the putt and a link in the chain. When pulling the putt, the body was practically horizontal to the floor, and it was often quite difficult to set it in motion, but a little extra power could be generated by grasping the roof supports situated on either side of the putt road, pulling hand over hand.

Making or tucking a guss rope was something of a specialist's job, and although I myself wore one for many years I must confess that I never really mastered the fine art of tucking a guss.

Carting was extremely hard work and although the guss had been almost tailor-made to fit the back, it continually bruised the skin, causing wheals and sores, and quite often at the end of a day's work, blood trickled from the wounds. The distance of the putt haulage varied but boys were often expected to haul coal for anything up to 100 yards to the pit bottom, or coal hole as it was commonly called, where it was tipped out, to be reloaded into the coal basket and raised to the surface.

As the workforce grew, so did the need to convey miners to their workplaces more quickly. A new method for men ascending and descending the pit shaft was introduced, known as the 'hooker' system. A long piece of chain was added to the end of the shaft haulage rope, and the miners, wearing a leather or rope girdle with a spring hook device attached, hooked themselves to the links, forming a cluster round the chain. The girdle was worn round the thighs so they adopted a more or less sitting position and held on with their hands as they were lowered down the shaft. This method would be considered most undignified and dangerous to us 20th century miners, used to riding up and down in our iron cages in comparative safety.

Two types of hemp or fibre ropes were used for pit shaft haulage during this period, one being the traditional round rope, the other consisting of a number of smaller ropes plaited together, about 6 or 8 inches wide and resembling a giant piece of crochet. Incidentally, the steel wire ropes which were introduced at a much later date followed the same patterns, although the use of the flat wire rope was discontinued in the early years of the 20th century.

Coal baskets, which had hitherto been used for raising coal to the surface, were now being replaced by larger and more efficient coal carriages in order to cope with increased production. These were referred to in some old miners' diaries as 'hudges'. An 18th century dictionary refers to the word as meaning a large quantity of anything, e.g. a hudge of money, so it seems probable that the new device derived its name from the fact that it carried a large amount of coal. It was usually though not necessarily made of iron. A similar but modified version of the hudge was later introduced as a man riding vehicle.

Gunpowder, used in some Cornish tin mines by 1689, was only later introduced into Somerset mines. Initial experiments proved both difficult and dangerous, resulting in many accidents, some fatal, and it was only by the end of the 18th century that any degree of perfection or any measure of safety was achieved.

Firedamp, a form of hydrogen gas given off by certain types of coal and which becomes explosive when mixed with various proportions of air, was not supposedly found in the Somerset mines. There were, however, some minor explosions during the early years in the Mendip coalfield when work began on the lower seams where the gas content was much higher. Almost daily, miners suffered burns to their arms and bodies, some quite severe, which were treated with very primitive ointments. As an old miner once told me years ago, one of whose ancestors had experienced such burns, they were inflicted by jet-like gases being released from the coal seam as it was struck by the miner with his pick, and then ignited by the naked flame of his candle, which was his only flicker of light. These explosive conditions were most probably caused by poor ventilation

18

and in 1773, the miners of the Mendip coalfield were shocked by the death of four colleagues at Vobster after a serious gas explosion.

By 1750, the industry was showing some signs of improvement and speculators in various parts of North Somerset were becoming more keenly interested. New mines were established in Welton, Paulton, High Littleton, Clutton and Timsbury while the well-established Mendip mines were now working the lower seams. At Radstock, the experts of the day thought it most unlikely that any coal seams existed in the area. Nothing was known of the geological conditions and would-be speculators were reluctant to join in a coal race. It was well past the middle of the century before any attempt was made to prove the ground.

By 1760, however, a pit shaft was being sunk, and some two or three years later the first coal seam was struck at a depth of some 150 yards. The first strike was named the Great Vein, subsequently better known to its miners as the Gurt Vein. This discovery spurred the prospectors on to sink to greater depths and at 360 yards or so, five more seams were found, Top Little, Slyving, Middle, Under Little and Bull veins. The best of these proved to be the Great and Bull veins, both of which averaged about two feet thick and became the best coal-producing seams in the Radstock area. This mine became known as Old Pit, an odd name one might think for a new venture, and was the start of an exciting industry which was to last over 200 years.

Despite the modest measure of improvement made in the industry during the first half of the 18th century, the latter half was not so encouraging. This was probably due to the fact that the mine workings were getting farther from the pit bottom, thus increasing the haulage distance and adding to the ever-present problems of ventilation and drainage. The coal winding system was also inadequate to deal with any increase in production, but at that time it was difficult to see how it could be improved.

Although James Watt had invented his steam engine (which was mainly used, in mining projects, for pumping water) by 1769, it was some 12 years before his engine was introduced to Somerset. Its introduction was probably

19

welcomed with some relief by many colliery owners although not everyone was able to take immediate advantage, possibly for financial reasons, and it did not prevent a good many mines from being closed at a much later date because of drowned out workings. They were known locally as 'fire engines', probably because their fire box, boiler and pumping gear all comprised one unit, and a fire had to be lit under it before it would function.

Now that the steam engine had been established, modified and improved models were bound to follow, and it was not surprising that a steam winding engine was introduced a few years later. The first steam winder was installed at Old Pit, Radstock, in 1782. It was recorded that its performance left a lot to be desired but it was not long before a more efficient engine was introduced into some mines.

The introduction of steam winding meant that the amount of coal which was hauled up the pit shaft in one day could be doubled or even trebled, and it must be assumed that the workforce would have been increased. Carting boys were still pulling putts of coal from the face to the pit bottom, and if there was to be any increase in production, some form of quicker transport was needed. It was probably at this stage that the wheeled cart or tram was brought into use. The first wheeled carts were of a shallow type, probably holding two or three hundredweight of coal, and fitted with flat, iron wheels. They did not yet run on rails but were pulled and/or pushed by boys who became known as runners or pushers. This did not mean the abolition of the putt or the guss and crook as they were still used for hauling coal from the workings to the road loading points right up to the 1930s.

These changes were all part of a gradual process, the Somerset coal owners being very reluctant to take advantage of any form of modernisation. The same might be said of the miners who eyed any form of expansion or development as a threat to their meagre livelihood. Although the steam engine did much to revolutionise the Somerset coal industry, its overall prosperity was still not very encouraging. Competition became very fierce as more pits came into production and transport facilities had not shown a great deal of improvement. The industry still relied on horse-drawn waggons to distribute coal to nearby towns, while the most important and largest markets were still very much out of reach.

By 1790, however, rumours were rampant that a canal was to be constructed which could give them the desired outlet, and a little later the Somersetshire Coal Canal Company revealed its plans. A canal was to be constructed from Dundas, on the Kennet & Avon Canal, to Midford, thence along the valley to Dunkerton, Camerton and on to Paulton Engine where two collieries were already in production near the banks of the proposed canal. These two mines were then known as Paulton Upper Engine and Paulton Lower Engine, both deriving their names from installing the latest models of steam engine. Today the area is known as Goosard, and the site of Paulton Upper Engine mine is now the site of the Paulton sewage works. This new canal project was probably the lifesaver for many mines in High Littleton, Timsbury, Camerton and Paulton and there was much speculation as to their future prosperity. Some companies even went to the extent of sinking new shafts, five new ones being sunk or nearing completion at this time. This brought the total number of mines to be served by the canal to twelve.

The second section of the SCC was to be constructed from Midford to Wellow, Foxcote, Radstock and Lower Welton, where about 6 collieries would be able to use its services.

Work began on the canals in 1795 and was completed by 1799. The Midford to Paulton canal was a big success; horse-drawn barges could now be brought up to the Paulton Basin and coal taken by waterway to markets in the Thames Valley. The project also gave iron foundries and engineering works more incentive to set up in the mining areas, eager to supply the mine companies with tram-rails, improved waggons and any necessary ironwork in their quest for prosperity.

At Radstock, however, they were not so fortunate. The canal was built but the soil proved to be so porous that it failed to hold its water. This was a big disappointment to all concerned after so much expense and hard work, but it was not to be an entirely wasted effort, for the Radstock coal owners agreed on an alternative plan. Some time later a tramroad was constructed on the towpath of the canal along which horses pulled laden coal waggons to Midford, where the coal was transferred to barges, thus giving them access to the privileged coal markets.

Quite a number of mines were some distance from the canal at Paulton or the tramroad at Radstock, but this was overcome by laying tramroads from the mines to the loading points. Others were not so fortunate and were obliged to continue using road transport.

How fortunate it was for the industry that these two natural valleys were so conveniently situated to provide transportation for two-thirds of the coalfield.

Going into the 19th century there were some 30 pits producing coal in Somerset, though probably many of the smaller ones were being run down at this time. Any that closed, however, were soon replaced by new pits. Although many improvements had been made, production had not risen as fast as it might have done in relation to the increase in the workforce. Mine workings were obviously getting further away from the pit bottoms, and the extra workforce was most probably wasted in manhandling the same amount of coal.

Unlike some other areas, there was not a great deal of rejoicing in the Mendip area of the coalfield in the year 1800. Their transport problems had not greatly improved and many of the mines were experiencing familiar problems with ventilation and drainage. The seams in many of the Mendip mines were almost vertical, and while it might be said that most of the basic techniques and skills used in other mines could be applied here, miners in this area were essentially a little more skilled and more knowledgeable of the prevailing geological conditions. This area was said to be the most geologically disturbed in the Somerset coalfield. The year 1800 also brought much sadness to this area when an explosion at Old Breach mine at Vobster claimed the lives of another 11 men.

Although detonators were introduced in 1800, it is most unlikely that they were used for shot-firing in Somerset mines at this stage. Indeed, it is very difficult to find out to what extent explosives were used at all, or how, or even what methods were used to bore holes into the rockface. It seems most likely that the hand and hammer drill were used. Some managements were probably not in favour of using too much explosive; they were more in favour of retaining smaller underground waggons which required smaller and lower roads, thereby limiting the amount of rock and rubbish to be hauled up the shaft to the surface. It is interesting to note that the rubbish tips left by the early mines, those closed by 1850, were much smaller than those which were eventually modernised and operated near or into the 20th century.

Coming up to the middle of the century, the coal canal and tramroad had reached their boom period and were stretched to their full capacity. Despite this, some measure of frustration was creeping in because some mines were not receiving adequate clearance of their coal stocks. The canal was unable to operate for long periods during the long and severe winters of the 19th century, when it was often frozen solid. This was indeed frustrating to all concerned, especially when coal was so essentially needed by both industrial and domestic consumers. Not only were coal contracts unfulfilled but the miners also suffered wage losses which they could ill afford. It is said that many of the miners spent their leisuretime skating on the ice in their hobnailed boots in order to keep fit and warm.

The Radstock tramroad was not so much troubled by ice as by heavy rain and deep snow, and it must have been difficult to maintain this very delicate railroad in the depths of winter.

During the early years of the 19th century, some mines were overcoming the problems of ventilation by sinking an extra shaft. The two shafts were then connected, one being known as a 'furnace shaft'. A fire was lit at the base of the furnace shaft which would therefore pull a strong draught of air from the mine workings. As it took in this air, it would suck fresh air down the other shaft, and if the airways underground were correctly designed and properly maintained, a supply of good, clean fresh air would be circulated continuously round the workings.

The problem of water drainage in underground workings was very much greater. Although steam-powered engines were now available for pumping out pit shafts, there was a growing need for more efficient facilities for pumping out more distant workings, especially those lower than the level of the pit shaft. At this time, underground workings were not charted and quite often, through no fault of their own, miners broke through into old workings which had been abandoned, releasing large quantities of trapped water, jeopardising lives and quite often causing pits temporarily to be closed. One of the worst examples was at the Hayeswood Colliery, Timsbury, in 1845, when 11 miners were drowned.

The coal industry nationally was now becoming more and more competitive in the face of increased demand for coal. But while most other coalfields were being served by the ever expanding railway system, the Somerset coalfield remained in a state of retarded uncertainty. However, in the years just before 1850, quite a lot of modernisation was taking place in a number of pits at Radstock. Small shafts were being enlarged and new and more efficient winding engines installed. The introduction of coal trams or waggons capable of holding half a ton of coal meant that underground roadways had to be rebuilt, both higher and wider, in order to maximise efficiency. New tram-rails were installed, tram chassis greatly improved, tram wheels were flanged on the inside as with railway wagons,and axles made more flexible, enabling them to negotiate corners more easily. Tramroads were now being constructed underground much like miniature railways, with wooden sleepers replacing the heavy, cumbersome stone ones. New and larger boilers for generating more steam power were installed, and for the first time in Somerset, steam was being piped underground where stationary steam winding-engines were bolted onto prepared engine beds and used for hauling coal trains up steep inclines. This meant that deepside workings, those descending away from the pit shaft as opposed to the ascending topside workings, could be developed to a much greater extent.

What, one wonders, gave the Radstock coal companies such incentive to carry out such a stringent programme of modernisation to many of their mines? Did they have advance information? Surely it was no coincidence that a railway branch line was constructed from Frome to Radstock in 1853. Radstock had been the latecomer to the coal industry; it had not enjoyed the best of fortune in the early years but with the coming of the railway it was ironic that it had now become the hub of the industry. Not only did the railways bring prosperity to the coal industry, but to the community as a whole. Eventually waggon works, repair shops and engineering works sprang into being as a result, all adding to the prosperity of the little country town.

Some shafts had been enlarged to the extent where two cages could be operated simultaneously, passing each other midway in the shaft. To operate two cages safely in one shaft, it was necessary to fit wooden guides in the pit shaft, one near the wall of the shaft and one in the centre, reaching down the whole depth of the shaft. The cages then slid up and down between the guides, thus avoiding any swaying and minimising any risk of a collision. It is probable that steel winding ropes were now introduced to cope with cages holding half a ton of coal. Some pits with small shafts, which were not enlarged, installed more efficient winding gear and introduced a single two-tier iron cage, with guides. Although it raised two trams of coal at each winding, it was more time-consuming and therefore not as efficient as the two-cage system. Some pits were eventually equipped with three-tier cages.

By 1862, coal production had risen considerably with most mines working at full capacity. Quite a large number of pits were coming to an end; mining had ceased at High Littleton and mines closed at Paulton, Timsbury, Radstock and Mendip, but the number of closures was outnumbered by others coming into production. Between 1850 and 1860 the workforce had increased to the region of 6,000 and there was no shortage of employment although a shift of population might occur where a new mine was at any great distance from one that had closed.

Much was done during the 19th century to improve the conditions in which the miners worked and lived, and although the improvements did not measure up to everyone's expectations, at least a better standard of industrial civilisation was beginning to emerge.

The government was also showing some concern, particularly in relation to the exploitation of child labour in the mines. One enquiry revealed that many children, some as young as seven, were working long hours in the mines, performing tasks far beyond their physical capacity. Although this enquiry was conducted early in the century, it was not until 1870, when compulsory education was introduced, that this practice was brought to an end. Some concern was also being shown as to the degree of safety being observed underground, and about the middle of the century, the need for some official supervision was being considered. A code of safety regulations was drawn up and mine inspectors appointed, whose responsibility it was to make periodic and surprise checks to ensure the regulations were carried out.

Underground surveys were also being carried out, which enabled maps to be drawn up of the workings in comparison with surface maps. This was a much welcomed safety measure in view of the fact that so many mines had hitherto suffered water incursions from old workings. No doubt this procedure was also welcomed by neighbouring landowners who quite often feared that their mineral rights had been encroached upon.

In 1873, the Frome–Radstock railway branch line was extended to Bristol and this was undoubtedly welcomed by the mines which were on or near its route. The five mines were Welton Hill, Springfield (Old Mills), Farrington Gurney, Greyfield (Clutton) and Frys Bottom (Chelwood), all of which took full advantage of improving their transport facilities by building their own railroad direct to the main line. The following year another railway project was under way when the Somerset & Dorset Railway Extension was opened from Bath Green Park station, crossing the old Midford canal route, to Radstock, Midsomer Norton and on through parts of the Mendip foothills.

The boom in prosperity during the latter years of the 19th century had left a number of pits in a state of exhaustion, and by 1890 many had closed. Further closures had taken place at Timsbury and coal mining on the eastern boundary of Paulton had ceased. It was stated then that the coal canal

26

was unable to give adequate clearance to the mines still producing coal in the valley. There were now only three mines working, two at Timsbury and one at Camerton, compared to the 12 originally served by the canal. This would infer that these three mines were producing more coal at the end of the century than the 12 were at its start.

The coal canal had proved its worth, but after 100 years of service it was being run down as the railway thrust itself along its banks. By the end of the century a branch line from Hallatrow to Camerton had been opened and was later extended to Bath via Limpley Stoke. Although it was mainly intended as a mineral line, it later carried a passenger service.

After 300 years of coalmining in Somerset, the industry was going forward into the 20th century with a technical knowledge which it had accumulated over those years, and a technical working system which had been built up by generations of dedicated men and which was not improved upon for many years.

Colliery	Shaft Diameters	Shaft Depths
AMESBURY	?	200 FT.
BARLAKE	5FT. 0.INS	435.FT.
BILBOA.	?	240FT.
BISHOP SUTTON (OLD)	?	304FT.
BISHOP SUTTON (NEW)	9FT. 0INS	877.FT.
BRAYSDOWN	10FT. 0INS	1,834FT.
BREACH (VOBSTER)	?	867.FT.
BREWER'S	?	102 FT.
BROMBEL	4FT. 6INS	?
BROMLEY	4FT. 6INS	475FT.
BURCHELLS	?	148 FT.
CAMERTON (OLD)	7FT. 0INS	921FT.
CAMERTON (NEW)	8FT. 0INS	1,818FT.
CLANDOWN	6FT. 0INS	1,437 FT.
CONYGRE (UPPER)	8FT. 0INS	1,038FT.
CONYGRE (LOWER)	8FT 0INS	1,128FT.
CROSSWAYS	5FT. 0INS	144FT.
STRAP	10FT 6INS	1,838 FT.
DUNKERTON	10FT 0INS	1651 FT.
EDFORD	6FT. 0INS	708.FT.
FARMBOROUGH	?	1413 FT
FARRINGTON	9FT. 0INS	588FT.
FOXCOTE	9FT. 0INS	900FT.
ERYS BOTTOM.	9FT 0INS	588FT.
GREYFIELD	10FT. 0INS	900FT.
HAYESWOOD	6FT. 0INS	642FT.
HUISH	8FT 0INS	570FT.
KILMERSDON	10FT 6INS	1,582 FT.
LITTLEBROOK	5FT x 5FT.	215FT.
LUCKINGTON	6FT. 0INS	135FT.
LUDLOWS	8FT. 0INS	1686FT.
MACKINTOSH	8FT 3INS	1,620FT.
MEARNS	4FT. 6INS.	270FT.
MELLS	9FT. 0INS	540FT.
MIDDLE PIT.	10FT. 0INS	1,791. FT.
MOORESLAND	5FT. 0INS	231FT.
MOOREWOOD (OLD)	4FT 6INS.	365FT.
MOOREWOOD (NEW)	9FT. 0INS	888FT.
NETTLEBRIDGE	6FT 0INS	705FT.
NEWBURY (OLD)	?	250FT.
NEWBURY	9FT. 0INS	720FT.
NEW ROCK	4FT 6INS	1182 FT.
NORTON HILL (OLD)	4FT. 6INS	1247FT.

28

NORTON HILL (NEW)	13FT. 6INS	1,503. FT.
OLD GROVE	4FT 6INS	1,373. FT.
OLD MILLS	11FT. 0INS	1,098 FT
OLD PIT.	6FT. 0INS	942 FT.
OLD ROCK.	4FT. 6INS	711. FT.
OLD WELTON.	4FT. 6INS	1,646FT.
PAULTON BOTTOM.	4FT. 6INS	60FT.
PAULTON ENGINE	9FT. 0INS.	609FT.
PAULTON HAM.	6FT. 0INS	552FT.
PAULTON HILL	?	798 FT.
PENSFORD	14FT. 0INS	1,494FT.
PITCOT	5FT. 0INS.	555 FT
PRISTON	8FT 0INS	760FT
RADFORD	6FT. 0INS	1,152FT.
RINGING	?	360FT
RYDONS	?	312FT.
SALISBURY	6FT. 0INS.	150FT.
SHOSCOMBE	10FT × 7FT	360FT.
SIMONS HILL	4FT. 6INS	672FT.
SMALLCOMBE	7FT. 0INS	1,074FT.
SPRINGFIELD	9FT 6INS	965 FT.
TYNING NEW (FERSBURY)	4FT. 6INS	630FT
TYNING (RADSTOCK)	8FT. 0INS.	1,007FT.
VOBSTER	10FT. 0INS	990FT
WELLSWAY	4FT. 6INS	754FT.
WELTON HILL	6FT. 0INS.	608FT.
WITHY MILLS	4FT. 6INS.	804FT.
WOODBOROUGH	5FT 3INS	426FT.
WRITHLINGTON (LOWER)	10FT. 0INS	1,461.FT.
WRITHLINGTON (UPPER.)	11FT. 3INS	942FT.

KILMERSDON SHAFT SINKING BEGUN ON 6⁰ FEB 1874 ON THE PUMPING SHAFT. SINKING COAL WINDING SHAFT OCTOBER 1876. NORTON HILL SHAFT 1900 AND CLOSED 1966. LUDLOWS CLOSED 1954. TYNING CLOSED 1922. UPPER WRITHLINGTON CLOSED 1898. HUISH CLOSED FEBRUARY 1912. BRANSDOWN CLOSED 29. OCT 1959. FOXCOTE CLOSED FEB 1931. KILMERSDON CLOSED 1973. SEPTEMBER 28⁰. NEW ROCK CLOSED 28 SEPT 1968. OLD MILLS CLOSED APRIL 1966. PENSFORD CLOSED 13 DECEMBER 1959. MELLS CLOSED 30 OCT 1943. NEWBURY & MACKINTOSH CLOSED AUGUST BANK HOLIDAY 1927. GREYFIELD CLOSED 28 MAY 1911. MIDDLE PIT CLOSED JUNE 1933. CAMERTON CLOSED 14 APRIL 1950. DUNKERTON MAY 1928 (CLOSED) BROMLEY 18 MAY 1957

Details of shaft depth and width taken from a
notice at Clandown Colliery

2. Some Aspects of the Somerset Coalmines

In this chapter I explain some particular features about the system of coal workings in Somerset before going on in the next to discuss the 20th century history of the mines and coal production in detail. Most of these features were to be found as the mines entered the 20th century.

Cages

Although iron and steel headgear had been introduced to Somerset mines in a variety of designs, some pits still retained their original wooden structures, although of course all pits had by this time adopted the use of steel ropes and pulley wheels, and had been equipped with more modern winding engines. Iron cages and steel wire guide ropes had also been introduced, but here again some pits still retained the older wooden guides, especially where the pit shafts were not quite vertical. Quite a number of the older shafts had little kinks in them.

All cages were built of steel, their size being governed by the size of the shaft. They were operated by a wire rope wound onto the drum of the winding engine. To avoid them swaying in the shaft, four wire guides were fitted from the pithead gear and suspended down the shaft to the area at the pit bottom known as the sump, where they were made fast and kept rigid. At the top and bottom of each cage, a well-greased guide shoe was fitted round each wire, thus holding the cage firmly in position. The sides, top and bottom of the cages were steel-plated, but the front and back were fitted with lift-off iron gates which were used at all times when men were riding but were removed when winding coal. Tram rails were fitted to the floor of each deck of a cage so that they coincided with and were in line with the tramroads both at the pit bottom and on the surface. To ensure that they were level when the cage was being loaded or unloaded, some support was necessary.

To provide this support at the top of the shaft, a mechanism commonly known as 'dogs' was fixed on steel girders, firmly set into the walls just below the surface. Four flat-topped arms were attached and the whole assembly worked with a hand lever. The dogs were held in the 'off' position until the cage was pulled just clear of the surface; they were then levered into the 'on' position, the arms extended and the cage lowered to rest on the arms. A similar mechanism was used at the pit bottom where two or three-tier cages were used. Loading and unloading a cage was done by four men, two on the surface and two at the bottom. The underground loader was known as the 'on setter', his job being to push loaded trams of coal into the cage, at the same time giving an empty tram a bump out, thereby helping his assistant on the other side of the shaft pull the empty from the cage. The safety bar was applied, the signal given to the surface and the cage was on its way again. On the surface the operation was reversed. Here, as the cage came to rest on the dogs, the 'banksman' pulled off the loaded tram while his assistant pushed another empty in from the other side. This then was the daily routine on a coal-producing shift. The work was carried out with such precision that the cage hardly ever seemed to stop.

Water pumps

Many pits had now installed improved steam pumps, the most popular and reliable being the Cornish pump, although this could only be used where a shaft was available for the sole purpose of pumping. These pumps were housed in a spacious building on the surface and were probably expensive to operate and maintain. Other types of pump were also used, those with a suction action operating on the surface while others, designed to push water up the shaft, were positioned underground. Some were quite often stationed in caves or unused coal holes part-way up the shafts. Compressed air was also a source of power for pumping though I recall it only being used to pump out small amounts of water in some of the lower workings. Even here the cold air quite often froze the water and it was quite common to see chunks of ice being ejected from the pump's exhaust. Cages were also sometimes used in various unorthodox methods to alleviate crises caused by sudden influxes of water. Water carriers could be fixed to the underside of the cage, or water tanks mounted on tram chassis. Sometimes the cage could be removed and replaced by water-carrying vehicles. These improvised methods would probably only be implemented between coal-producing shifts or at weekends when the pits were idle.

Signals

Pit shaft signals were very important from a safety point of view. For centuries they had been fairly primitive, though on the whole efficient, and the device inherited by the 20th century was a simple one, known as the 'rapper'. This consisted of a flat sheet of iron, about 18 inches long, 12 inches wide and an inch thick to which was attached a hinged 4lb sledgehammer. One of these would be positioned at the bottom of the pit near the on setter and linked to a lever at the top of the pit by a thin wire pinned to the wall of the shaft with brackets to which small wheels were attached to ensure freedom of movement. The lever at the top was within easy reach of the banksman. When the lever was released, the hammer fell onto the flat sheet with a loud bang. When this action was repeated in quick succession any number of signals could be made. This was the 'down' signal and a similar 'up' signal was fitted in reverse. In this case the hammer device was fixed high on the headgear so that it could be heard by both the banksman and the driver in the engine house, and to prevent any improper use of the signals which could have cost lives.

A code of universally used signals was as follows: one rap to raise the cage, two raps to lower the cage with three additional raps if men were riding. In an emergency, when cages were in motion, one rap meant 'stop'. Pre-arranged signals were also used by engineers, fitters and mine officials when inspecting or working in the shaft.

As the 20th century progressed, most mines built their own power houses and generated electricity at the pithead. Gradually, steam pumping, underground steam haulage, all primitive signals and even some pit winding engines gave way to electrical systems.

Ventilation

As I have already mentioned ventilation was often a problem in the pits until the introduction of a second, furnace, shaft. This system operated by linking all underground working areas together and forcing the air round in a single direction. The air flow was directed from the pit bottom, along the main road to the farthest workings. Any roads leading off were partitioned by fixing wooden frames at each entrance and covering them with brattice cloth which was treated with a tar preservative and resembled roofing felt. This was nailed to the top of the frame with the sides left loose so that it acted as a flap. After a tram had passed through, it fell into place again, sealing the entrance. These partitions were commonly known as curtains. They allowed the air to pass through but not back, thereby forcing the air along its correct route. In some workings where the air flow was particularly strong and brattice cloth proved ineffectual, strong wooden doors were installed. It was also important that districts which had been exhausted of coal or abandoned, were completely sealed off to prevent the waste of precious air; this was done by tightly packing the entrances of all unused roads with waste rubble and stones.

Quite a considerable amount of fresh air was also generated by the cages as they descended and ascended at speed in the shaft. Proof of this was recognised on occasions when accidents occurred and a cage or tram fell down a shaft. The shock wave of air, similar to a bomb blast, could be felt throughout the workings. Fast moving trains of trams also made a modest contribution to maintaining a good air flow.

All airways were meant to be inspected regularly but were quite often neglected and there were occasions when repairs were not executed quickly enough to prevent heavy falls of rock from temporarily closing some coal-producing areas.

Neither candles nor oil-lamps would burn in foul air but the carbide gas lamp would remain alight for quite a long period in an atmosphere where there was little oxygen. If this deteriorated below a certain level, the flame on the lamp became very weak and pale blue before being extinguished. In such circumstances it was unsafe to stay in the area. The physical effects on the human body of working in foul air underground resulted in extreme muscular fatigue and drowsiness, the symptoms becoming more apparent on reaching the surface.

The furnace system of ventilation continued well into the 20th century but was eventually phased out in favour of powerful air extraction fans.

Lighting

Nowhere is light more appreciated than when you are working underground in a deep mine. On the surface we often hear people refer to the night darkness as pitch black but this does not compare with the darkness underground where it is absolutely total. Down through the ages many people have been fearful of the dark and I think the same may be said of most miners, who have at some time during their career been alone in a mine when their light has been extinguished or failed and they have been plunged into total darkness.

To give you some idea of the difference between the darkness on the surface and the darkness underground, let me relate an occasion which I experienced as a lad of 16. At the time I was working in a coal-producing road leading off a very steep incline about one mile from the pit bottom. Halfway through our shift the main haulage system had broken down and although the two men with whom I worked had continued to hew coal during the breakdown, I as their carting boy had been unable to send out our normal coal output because there had not been enough empty coal waggons. Just as we were about to finish and go home, the fault was rectified and empty waggons were brought to us. At that time we were being paid a small bonus of a few shillings a week if we exceeded a certain number of tons so, being enthusiastic, I decided to stay at work a little while longer and fill some of the waggons with the coal which had accumulated. The other two men did not approve of me working alone, pointing out that I would be contravening industrial law, but I promised not to stay long and went on to load four waggons with coal, about two tons. I felt quite pleased with my achievement, put on my clothes and started to make my way to the pit bottom. I had not gone far, however, when my light went out and I had no matches with which to relight it.

Quite contrary to what I thought I would do if ever I found myself in such circumstances, I immediately went into a state of panic, lost my sense of direction and went down on my knees. In the total darkness and eery silence I imagined that the roof and the sides of the road were gradually caving in on me. A few flakes of rock shale falling on the floor a little distance away, coupled with a creek or two from wooden roof supports which would normally go unnoticed, sounded like an imminent fall of hundreds of tons of rock. After a few minutes I gathered my wits and began to crawl, feeling for the tram rails as my guide. Eventually I bumped into the loaded coal waggons in the small siding where they normally waited to be pulled up the incline. I felt my way along the small train of waggons, found the points which guided them into the incline main road, and knew then that I was going in the right direction, crawling up the long, steep incline. While making my way up in the darkness, I saw what I thought were lights on some of the old wooden roof supports. These 'lights' looked so real that I even tried to light my lamp from them. I discovered later that they

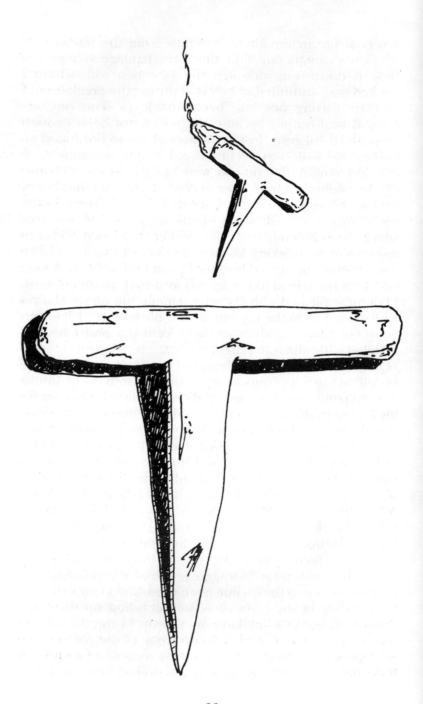

were patches of luminous fungus growing on the bark of the old damp tree trunks. My ordeal thankfully came to an end when the afternoon shift put in an appearance a little later.

It is very difficult to explain the phenomenal difference of the environment on the surface from that which prevails underground; it is my conclusion that the total darkness and the deathly silence underground must have a detrimental effect on the brain.

Centuries ago the first lights to be used in the Somerset mines were candles. These were crudely made from yellowish tallow, a by-product of cow fats, and the thick wick was probably coated with beeswax. They smoked profusely when lit, smelt unpleasant and burned out very quickly, but were used over a period of some 200 years. Although slightly improved in the 18th century, it was not until the middle of the 19th century that the candle as we know it today was perfected. In 1830 a German scientist was experimenting with coal and other bituminous products when he discovered that they contain a certain amount of oil and produce, among other by-products, a substance called paraffin wax. By the 1840s the paraffin wax candle had become available, a vast improvement on the tallow candle as it was more solid, burnt much brighter with little smoke or smell, and was a much better shape; what is more, it now had some affinity to coal. This candle was used in the Somerset coalfield as late as the 1920s.

The candles were carried undergound in a miner's candlestick which was made of metal, about six inches long and tapering to a sharp point. The end holding the candle was split into two parts so that when they were held apart a candle could be inserted. The candlestick was worn on the side of the head, the pointed end being pushed through a couple of leather loops on the miner's cap, but it was customary for the miners hewing at the coalface to stick the pointed end firmly into the wooden pit props because, as the candle burned and melted, the grease often ran unpleasantly down the side of the face. The candle would not burn in foul air and long after the introduction of oil and gas lamps, most miners carried a piece of candle in their waistcoat pocket so that they could test the air if they wished. Looking back it seems almost inconceivable that so much could have been accomplished from the flickering light of a candle.

After it was discovered that coal contained oil, it was not long before many of its by-products were being refined and perfected, and it was not surprising that oil-burning lamps were introduced for domestic and industrial use. During the second half of the 19th century an oil lamp was introduced into the Somerset mines and, although it was not popular with the majority of miners, it was used for quite a number of years. The lamp was made from a very light metal and consisted of a globe-shaped body, about three inches in diameter, which contained the oil; a small tubular neck about two inches high; at the top of the neck a smaller hole where a rather thick wick was inserted and pushed down to reach the oil; and on the bottom, a tubular stem about four inches long which was again passed down through a loop on the miner's cap and was normally worn on the forehead. The lamp burned quite economically for a long time and was not easily extinguished, but produced a thick, black smoke and an unpleasant smell of burning oil.

The carbide gas lamp, an American product, was first used in the Somerset mines in the early years of the 20th century. It was made of brass and consisted of two parts; the upper part was a cylinder-shaped reservoir of water and the bottom contained the carbide. This very much resembled small pieces of metal ore and when added to water gave off an acetylene gas. A water regulator controlled the flow of water, allowing small drops to land on the carbide. The gas, in a bid to escape, was forced out of a burner in a long, straight streak which, when lit, produced a flame four inches long. This form of light was probably the best ever used in the Somerset mines as it provided a good, all-round, efficient arc of light.

The carbide for these lamps, about four ounces, was issued daily free of charge, but the cost of the lamps was borne by the miners. They were expensive in the early years, costing as much as one third of a man's weekly wages, which invariably caused hardship to families when they had to be renewed. After nationalisation in 1947, the coal board sold them to miners at cost price for a time, but later they were issued free.

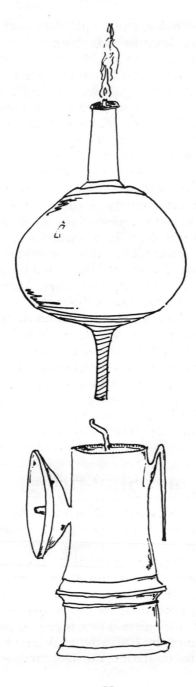

After 1947, electric lamps were gradually introduced. First used by managers, deputies and shot-firers, presumably for a trial period, they were soon issued to all miners in the Somerset coalfield. As a measure of safety, after this no naked lights were allowed underground, though ironically, fitters were seen on occasions doing the odd welding job underground at weekends. The banning of naked lights underground caused a great deal of frustration to those miners who enjoyed a cigarette or pipe of tobacco while working, and I do not think the electric lamp was ever appreciated. It consisted of a small bulb and reflector worn on the forehead with a length of cable leading to a battery clipped to a leather belt worn around the waist. These battery lamps were very heavy and cumbersome, and disliked by most miners. They gave a good frontal spotlight but not such a good arc of light all round. After this, all coalface examiners were obliged to carry Davy safety lamps so that regular tests could be made for gas and foul air. The Davy lamp had been invented chiefly through the instigation of the Bishop of Bristol, Dr Gray. In 1815 he became concerned at the number of deaths and injuries caused by gas explosions in neighbouring mines, mainly from what was known as firedamp. Being something of a scientist himself, he made a number of experiments and collaborated with Sir Humphrey Davy after whom their eventual successful invention was named.

Branching and Shot-firing

Branching was the term used when it was necessary to make roadways, airways, penetrate major faults, or make connecting roads between one seam of coal and another, through hard, solid rock. The men who carried out this work, always those with vast mining experience, were known as 'branchers'. Once the sinking operations for a new pit shaft were completed, the roadways, airways and pump houses needed for the initial development around the pit bottom would mainly be constructed by branching through solid rock, especially if the area was infested with geological faults, as was often the case. Before a branch was constructed, the underground plans were consulted and a mining surveyor would instruct the branchers as to the height, width and length required, and whether the floor was to be level or inclined. The branchers would then begin by boring holes into the rockface. The number of holes depended on the dimensions of the branch, but it was normal practice to bore some at the bottom, some at the centre, and some at the top. In the early years of the 20th century they were bored with a hand machine which was a very arduous task.

When the holes had been bored, packets of explosives connected to a length of fuse wire were pushed in to the full length of the holes, usually about a yard, with a ramming stick, and then soft clay used to fill up the holes. The tails of fuse wires were cut to different lengths, those from the bottom holes being the shortest, then the centre ones a little longer, and the top ones the longest. It was always essential that the fuse wires were long enough to allow the firer time to get well away to a place of safety before the explosion took place. The differing lengths of fuse wire were to allow the explosives to fire in succession which normally gave a better result. After the shots had been fired the first task was to rip down any loose rock hanging overhead and to break up any large stones too big to handle. All the rubble was then loaded into trams and dispatched to the surface. An 8-foot square branch could yield anything from 12 to 16 tons of rock after each firing which would result in advancing the branch just one yard.

As the branch progressed, sighting lines were hung from the roof. These had little weights attached to them to keep them taut and everyday before boring the holes, they were lined up and while one man held his light against the rockface, another sighted along the strings and the centre of the branch was then indicated with a chalk mark to ensure that it was being kept on a straight course.

One of the greatest difficulties as the branch progressed was ventilation, and the further it went the more difficult it became. After each round of firing, volumes of smoke and dust stagnated in the work area and were very slow to clear.

41

Unfortunately, in the early years mechanical aids were few, probably because of lack of investment rather than lack of invention, and the only method of dispersing the foul smoke was by a hand-driven fan, fondly known as a 'Blow Georgie'. This consisted of a rotary fan about 18 inches in diameter encased in a metal tube to which other tubes, 6 feet in length, could be added as the branch progressed. It was worked by a boy turning its handle continuously for a whole shift. Not only was this a very arm-aching and boring task but one that caused him to be the victim of the suffocating smoke as he succeeded in vacuuming it out. It was a primitive method and only maintained a very limited circulation.

When branching in solid virgin strata, roof supports were seldom needed as the rock remained hard, but no doubt props would be needed at a later stage when the area round the branch was developed and subsidence began to occur.

As a boy, I worked for a short period turning the fan for two old branchers who were heading in towards a coal seam in an undeveloped area. Neither they nor the officials knew the precise distance to the coal but one day an official carrying out an inspection declared that they were off course and would be unlikely to find coal. The branchers were adamant, arguing that they were on course and that the coal was only eight yards away. The official shook his head in doubt as he left. A little later, when we had our break for food, I asked them how they could be so sure that they were correct. 'It's something which cannot be explained; it must be a gift which is gained by experience' was all they could say. After we had eaten our sandwiches and were about to restart our work, they took me into the branch which was then about 30 yards long and at about the halfway stage. They asked me to take note of the echo which resounded with quite a metallic ring to it, but as we moved in to within six yards of the rockface the echo had a much more mellow ring. 'That's why we know we're right', they said. I admitted the echo was different but at the time was not greatly impressed. Two days later, after the firing had been carried out and the debris cleaned up, I was invited back to the rockface and we stood touching the wall of stone. This time there was no echo and a complete change in the atmosphere. They assured me they were no more than four yards from the coal. The complete change in the air left me with a very uncanny feeling and this time I was impressed. Two days later, after firing the usual round of shots, the branchers came out triumphantly; the coal had been found and they were accurate almost to the inch.

Not many miners were willing to undertake this type of work because they were aware of the damaging effect it could have on their health, and few miners who followed this occupation escaped without contracting the dreaded disease of silicosis. This disease was contracted by the men constantly inhaling minute particles of stone dust, invisible to the naked eye. A medical expert in lung diseases once told me that each of those particles of dust had sharp, barbed edges which dug into the delicate tissues of the lung and if continuously inhaled, their accumulation made breathing very difficult. It was also said that a million of these particles would be no larger than a pin's head. Many branchers died comparatively young, while those who survived suffered long and painful lives.

Shot-firing in advancing roads in development areas was carried out in the same way as in the branch except that, in these roads, the coal seam had already been removed so that the amount of rock to be blown down was much smaller and therefore easier to remove. In the early years, competent, experienced miners were permitted to carry explosives and entrusted to fire their own shots, but as the number of accidents increased, this practice was stopped and only professionally trained men carried out the work. Accidents became far less frequent although the occasional mishap did occur when 'misfires' were approached carelessly after a faulty or damp fuse had merely delayed the explosion. Most of these accidents too were eliminated after a time limit was imposed forbidding anyone to approach a misfire until after a given lapse of time. Responsibility for shot-firing was eventually taken over by the pit deputies who were qualified to supervise large areas of mine workings. In mines where coal was only produced on one shift, the bulk of firing was done on the afternoon shift, but when coal was being produced round the clock, as it quite often was, it had to be done more or less between shifts and normally kept to a minimum during a coal-producing period.

Geological Conditions

The Somerset coalfield was reputed to contain more geological faults than any other in England, and judging by the number which were encountered in our generation, I can readily believe this to be true. The most faulted area in Somerset was probably the most southerly, in the Mendip area. Here, in this very disturbed strata, there were several major and numerous minor faults, while the coal measures were so badly distorted that in some mines the seams were almost vertical, adding to the already complex mining conditions. In the Radstock area, the unique Radstock Slide and great Clandown faults were responsible for a great deal of disruption over a wide area, while in the more northerly region, the great Farmborough and Priston faults had a most adverse effect on the coal measures almost as far as the northernmost mine at Pensford.

When a coal seam was lost and a major fault encountered underground, it was the normal practice to try and prove it before making any commitment to blast through it. This was done by driving very long bore holes into the fault in all directions, and if the result of any bore hole proved positive the seam would be pursued.

There were several types of minor fault, most of which could be dealt with successfully at the coalface, but of course not without some discomfort to the miners and loss of coal production. As they very rarely ran in a straight line, not every miner working at the coalface would encounter it at the same time and it might be many days or weeks before the seam regained its normality. Usually, experienced miners would instinctively know by various symptoms and changes in their working conditions many days before a fault was encountered. These small faults were generally preceded by deteriorating roof conditions, sometimes a little less quality in the coal, some dampness on the floor, and quite often the odd drop of water from the roof. As the

44

last coals were stripped off, a wall of very hard, clay-like stone was invariably revealed and at this point the original roof would end. This type of fault was probably a crevice caused by an earthquake and later filled in. As the wall of clay was removed, which might be only a few feet or at most a couple of yards deep, the coal seam appeared again and the normal roof could be caught up as progress was made. Sometimes with this type of fault, where the disturbance had been severe, only half the seam would disappear, to be found a step up or down, depending on the direction in which one was working. In some instances the whole seam would be found a couple of feet higher or lower. If a leader fault was met, radiating from a major one, the stone would be of a much harder nature and it would be necessary to blast through it. In addition to these faults, there were various types of breaks in the strata above the coal, some concave, others convex. Though they were equally dangerous, the convex break was probably the most treacherous, causing the roof to break up more quickly. These breaks could not often be detected until the coal had been removed from under them, by which time they were almost uncontrollable and very dangerous. In some mines, small areas of stone above the coal were very badly shattered, making roof control very difficult, while in others they were fortunate enough to have what was known as Greys stone over some coal seams. This was a stone of an exceptionally hard nature, so hard it was said that the use of pit props was unnecessary, though it was extremely difficult to bore holes into it.

Coal seams varied slightly from one area to another, some being much harder than others. Oddly enough, the floor of the hard coals was also very hard while the softer coals usually had a very thin layer of clay-like substance on the floor. Some seams had bands of very hard and heavy clay immediately above them, others had shale stone, neither of which could be propped up. One or two were divided in the centre by a very black, shiny shale which was usually fairly easy to hew and was commonly known as cockroach benching, so called because it very much resembled live cockroaches as it slithered to the floor when hewn.

Tramroads, Transport and Haulage

The vast network of tramroads which lay beneath the Somerset coalfield were in fact miniature railway systems. These railroads were laid in all main or arterial roads, from the pit shaft to the farthest working outposts, serving all working districts en route. The roads were laid not only for hauling coal but also for carrying mining supplies such as timbers for roof supports; sleepers and rails for extending roadheads; and machinery, such as pumps and pipes, without which coal could not be produced.

Lengths of flanged rails, normally 18 to 20 feet long, were fixed to 4-foot long transverse sleepers with L-shaped nails. Bending rails to take tramroads round long bends was done with an implement known as a 'Jim Crow', a horseshoe-shaped tool with a gigantic central screw. Several types of rope haulage were used in the early years of the century, and in fact retained and still operated when the coalfield was closed down. Transportation of coal began at the coalface whence it was carted by putt to the road and loaded into trams; the loads were then manually pushed by men known as 'runners' to the sidings. There were two haulage systems used up to the main roads, one of which could only be operated in a long-haul incline, that is one where loads could be hitched to a rope at the bottom and be pulled to the top in a continuous stream. The haulage was in fact an end-less rope, fitted round a grooved, horizontal wheel fixed at ground level at both ends of the road. This required a double tramroad, one to take the loads up, the other for the returning empties. As the loaded trams were run out over points and aligned with the tramroad incline, a clip was hitched to the crook on the tram chassis and then clipped and screwed tightly onto the rope. Loads were spaced to avoid overloading and as they reached the top, on the level, the clips were removed and hitched to empties for their descent. The rope ran continuously, stopping only in an emergency, thus ensuring a constant stream of traffic up and down all day.

The second type of haulage to the main road operated with a single tramroad where loads were pulled up and empties let down on a single rope, wound on the drum of an electrically-powered engine designed to serve many lateral roads alternately.

Another rope haulage system, known as a 'main and tail', was used in a main road which was fairly straight and therefore capable of hauling quite a long train of trams. It was operated by an electric engine and the rope, which was twice as long as the distance to be hauled, worked on a drum, running overhead on a series of small pulley wheels or rollers. When a train of loads was ready to be pulled out, one end of the rope was coupled to the front of the train, and the other to the rear. When the train reached its destination, the ropes were transferred to a train of empties and the engine put into reverse.

In the inclines, small rollers were fixed horizontally to the sleepers at intervals to minimise wear and tear on the rope, but in spite of this, ropes frequently broke. When a rope broke, there was always sufficient spare on the drum to allow for splicing, which was done by a rope specialist. Such was the precision and professionalism used by the splicer that it was impossible to locate where the joint had been made.

Horses still transported vast quantities of coal in the Somerset mines every day, being considered to be of great value as a means of cheap transportation. It is difficult to put a number to the ponies employed in the mines but it is probable that most of the larger coal-producing mines were employing at least six each. The ponies were used for pulling trams in main roads where they were more or less level and working conditions were favourable, high and well ventilated. Many people outside the industry were often critical of both management and miners, claiming that horses were ill-treated underground, but in my experience this was not true. They worked the same hours as the miners and were never overworked. In fact some probably did less work than their counterparts on farms. They were well fed and regularly checked by vets, and were certainly treated with utmost kindness by everyone. They were normally stabled quite close to the pit shaft where most of the workforce would have to pass by en route to their places of work; not many passed without giving the horses a friendly pat on the neck. Many had their favourites and took them apples, carrots and other little tit-bits nearly every day.

My experience has shown that horses are very intelligent with powerful instincts. On one occasion, as a young man, I was employed as a hitcher at the entrance to an incline where a horse named Smiler hauled trams from the pit shaft to me. One day the man who worked Smiler came running in without the horse to send a message to the surface via the field telephone. Smiler was halfway along the road with a train of empty trams when for some reason he refused to go any further. The management were concerned that the horse might be ill, but the hostler was convinced he was in good health. He had examined him and even unhitched the train and led him back towards the shaft, which he did willingly, although still refusing to go forward into the workings. When the driver returned to the train of trams, the horse was still standing where he had left it, well away from the train, and once more he tried to lead him forward. As he did so, he noticed that dust and small rubble had started to trickle down between the timbers supporting the roof. Some minutes later there was a loud bang as the roof supports gave way and large boulders of rock came hurtling down, blocking the road and leaving a gaping hole in the roof. This was only one of many such instances which I remember and many other Somerset miners could relate similar experiences. Ironically, although horses made a big contribution to underground transportation, they often presented transport problems themselves when they had to be hauled up and down the pit shaft. In this case, the cage was usually removed and the horses held upright in a specially made sling or net. The fact that their transportation in the mine shaft was so difficult was the reason why they were not brought to the surface more often.

Transporting supplies to outpost workings also quite often presented problems. Anything which could be carried in a tram, such as head timbers (small roof supports), short lengths of ironwork, ropes, cables, small machinery, etc could all be handled without much trouble; the roof supports for timbering in the main roads, ranging from 8 to 12 feet in length, could also be cut to the approximate size on the surface and sent underground without presenting too many problems. But greater difficulties occurred with long lengths of tramroad rails, long pipes for pumping water, and pieces of timber, some 25 feet in length, used to prop up the roof in large open spaces. These caused a lot of inconvenience especially in some of the old pit shafts which had not been widened and were in some cases only four feet square.

Only supplies which were currently needed were normally taken underground on the morning shift, such as urgently-needed coal-producing tools and small roof supports. All other supplies were transported down on the afternoon and night shifts. Any pieces of great length were transported to their destination on specially constructed trams called 'timber dillies'. Dilly was an old word for a cart and in this case referred to trams without backs or fronts which could be coupled together.

Somerset County Council.

The County Education Committee.

COAL MINES ACT, 1911.

Certificate of Qualification of Fireman, Examiner, or Deputy, under Section 15 (1) (b).

This is to certify that

George Fear

residing at *10 South View Clandown*

has been duly examined, and has satisfied the examiner:

(1) (a) That he is able to make accurate tests (so far as practicable with a safety lamp) for inflammable gas;

(2) (b) That he is able to measure the quantity of air in an air current;

(c) That his hearing is such as to enable him to carry out efficiently the duties of Fireman, Examiner or Deputy.

C. H. Bothamley
County Education Secretary.

County Education Office,
Weston-super-Mare,

5 FEB 1913 _____ 191____

NOTE.—(1) (a) is to be struck out in the case of a candidate producing a certificate from the Manager of his mine that he is employed in a mine in which inflammable gas is unknown.

(2) (b) is to be struck out in the case of a candidate producing a certificate from the Manager of his mine that he was employed as a Fireman, Examiner or Deputy on the 16th December, 1911.

Somerset County Council.

The County Education Committee.

COAL MINES ACT, 1911.

ertificate of Qualification of Fireman, Examiner, or Deputy,
under Section 15 (1) (b).

This is to certify that

George Fear

esiding at 10 South View, Clandown, nr Bath.

as been duly examined, and has satisfied the examiner :

(1) ~~(a) That he is able to make accurate tests (so far as practicable with a safety lamp) for inflammable gas~~ ;

(2) (b) That he is able to measure the quantity of air in an air current ;

~~(c) That his hearing is such as to enable him to carry out efficiently the duties of Fireman, Examiner or Deputy.~~

H. Brothamley
County Education Secretary.

ounty Education Office,
Weston-super-Mare,
June 27th 191 3

NOTE.—(1) (a) is to be struck out in the case of a candidate producing a certificate from the Manager of his mine that he is employed in a mine in which inflammable gas is unknown.

(2) (b) is to be struck out in the case of a candidate producing a certificate from the Manager of his mine that he was employed as a Fireman, Examiner or Deputy on the 16th December, 1911.

3. 20th Century Mining

The young miners of the 20th century just starting their working lives walked to their places of work through underground corridors and main roads, many of which had been well trodden for half a century by previous generations, some even longer. The coal which once prevailed in these roads and their vicinity had long since been removed, and time had allowed subsidence to fill in the vacant spaces where the coal was once found, and had healed the scars inflicted by the miners' picks of yesteryear. But if the stout timbers supporting the roof looked fairly new, it was because the old timbers had decayed and been replaced. In some mines, where the coal reserves covered large areas, many of these old roads were being extended to their boundaries, while others were being used as arterial roads for transporting materials and coal to and from far distant workings. Although many of the surviving mines were old, most of them had been modernised, many new safety measures introduced, management was improving and coalmining techniques had reached near perfection, all factors which led to a vast improvement in working conditions. With the exception of those mines with vast reserves, most had by this time taken out the coal nearest the pit shaft and probably a vast amount of topside coal as well, that is coal from the seams which incline upwards from the pit bottom towards the surface. All this coal could be mined and brought down to the pit shaft by manual labour on self-acting inclines at very little cost. It would perhaps be a little unfair to criticise either the coal owners or management for plundering the cheapest and most easily produced coal, their motive being profit, but it must be said that at this time, machinery for transporting coal from the declining seams was inadequate and expensive.

In spite of the fact that the Somerset mines were reputed to be very backward and inefficient at this time, the future prosperity was viewed with some optimism by most people concerned with the industry, and so it was from here that 20th century mining began.

The experienced miner's tools were very few and consisted of a pick, sledgehammer, small axe or wood-cutting handsaw, and a shovel. The cost of these was borne by the miner with the exception of the shovel which was provided by the mining company. Stone-boring machines were also a very important piece of equipment, again bought by the miner. I recollect that because they were expensive, small groups of miners working close to each other clubbed together and shared the cost. Later, some companies did install compressed-air boring machines but these were not very satisfactory. All tools that needed to be sharpened regularly were dressed by the company blacksmith free of charge.

Coalmining in Somerset was a complex operation and had to be seen underground in its unique environment to be properly understood. Trying to express its complexity in words is just as complex as the work itself. Roads, corridors or galleries, call them what you may though Somerset miners always called them roads, were the first essentials when developing a mine. The coal was taken out systematically in blocks about 25 yards wide and 80 yards long. Therefore if it had been planned to take out, for example, 20 of these blocks this would probably yield something over 100 tons of coal from a two-foot thick seam, providing there were no geological disturbances. Let us now assume that a seam is being worked, reached from a branch some little distance from the pit bottom, and a lateral road has been started. Coal-producing faces are operated on the left-hand side and it has been planned to drive another road to the right-hand side in order to increase production; the road is to be 8 feet wide and 8 feet high. This task would be allotted to two experienced miners and a first-rate carting boy, and as they prepare to start the new road they would be facing a two-foot seam of coal and six feet of solid rock. The coal seam would be running obliquely across the front, inclining away towards the surface, on the left, which would become known as the topside, and declining on the right, to be known as the deepside. The first task would be to remove the 8 feet of coal which would form the front of the road, taking out about one yard forward; this would be a block of coal about 8 feet by 3. The length of time it would take to carry out this initial work depended on the nature of the coal and whether it was hard or soft. The softer type of coal, normally used for industrial purposes, could be plucked more easily from the seam, but the harder coals, used as domestic coals, would not yield so easily and would have to be under-cut by a unique method commonly known by Somerset miners as 'benching'. This was carried out by cutting out a band of coal, 4 or 6 inches thick, with a hand pick, starting at floor level and benching as far forward as possible. During this procedure, wooden wedges were placed at intervals underneath the overhanging coal as a measure of safety to the hands and arms in case the whole block of coal should fall unexpectedly. During the benching period, tests were also carried out to ascertain to what degree the coal had been loosened. This was done by placing one hand on the face of the seam and tapping the coal with the pick head; if the area of coal which had been benched sounded like a bass drum, it was a sure sign that it was ripe to be felled.

As soon as possible after the coal had been removed, temporary pit props known as head timber were erected in position to hold up the roof. These were normally freshly-cut branches from trees grown in local woodlands and were about 3 to 4 inches in diameter. They were cut to approximate size on the surface and then cut to the final specifications by the miners underground. To erect the props, a shallow indentation was made in the floor, the foot of the prop placed in it and the prop hammered into the vertical position, with a flat piece of wood known as a 'trap' or 'slab', about 12 inches by 6 by 2, on top. These props were normally spaced at about 4 feet either way but of course they could be spaced more closely together if the roof was likely to prove dangerous. Once the coal had been removed and the head props erected, this section would now be designated as the front of the road. The next step to be carried out in the road making was for each man to take out about 4 yards of coal from either side of the road, making a face of some 32 feet. This would be the amount of coal to be taken out daily. When this amount of coal had been taken out, the amount of daily advance would probably be from 3 to 4 feet and would normally be carried out on the morning shift, which was recognized as the main coal-producing shift. In addition to hewing the coal, the two experienced miners were responsible for boring the required number of holes for blasting down the rock in order to further the advancement of the road. After boring the holes, some extra head props were erected either side of the road to prevent the blast bringing down more than the required 8 feet. The blasting was usually done at the beginning of the afternoon shift and the rubble, which was probably more than 10 tons, removed. As much as possible was packed into the space either side of the road from where coal had previously been removed to help hold the roof. When all the debris had been removed, the roof and sides were tested to find out the condition of the rock. If it was thought to be hard and trustworthy (although this was never taken for granted) it might only be necessary to erect a prop on the topside, temporarily to steady the roof. Known as 'stipples', these were much stronger than head timber, being 8 to 10 inches in diameter and 8 feet long. If the rock was weak and thought to be unstable and dangerous, a more elaborate system of roof supports would be necessary.

Although 4 yards of coal was hewn daily from each side of the road, only 3 yards on the topside was packed with rubble, leaving a space of one yard to serve as an airway to ventilate future workings. The space left behind after the coal had been taken out was known as the 'gob', and to pack it after shot-firing, the larger stones were manhandled, being thrown from one man to another. The smaller rubble was then shovelled from the man in the road to the other one working on his knees (bearing in mind that it was only two feet high) who packed it as tightly as possible from floor to roof.

During road advancement it was obviously necessary to lay a tramroad. Initially this was done by laying short lengths of rail. As the road progressed, the short lengths were replaced by longer and more permanent ones.

Working three shifts continuously, an advancement of about 8 yards could be accomplished in a week using this procedure. This may not be thought to be a great achievement but was in fact quite a good week's work. When the road had advanced about 12 yards, the initial work for a new face, known as the 'long wall stepped', was due to begin, involving the first of the 80 by 25 yard blocks of coal mentioned earlier. At this point a smaller road was turned off from the main road, on the topside, known as a 'toppo' although always pronounced by Somerset miners as 'topple'. The term referred to a collective number of workplaces.

The first task when the toppo was begun was to build a 'cog' to form the initial corner support. This comprised several stout tree branches about 4 to 5 feet long and 6 inches in diameter, laid alternately in pairs across each other until they were roof high. Stones were wedged between the timbers and rubble shovelled into the centre of the cog to help cushion the weight of subsidence which might occur in the next six months or so while the toppo was being worked out. Having formed one side of the toppo way, the next two yards of the gob were not packed as this was to be the width of the toppo. When sufficient progress had been made in the roadway, a second cog was built and the toppo way formed. When the main road had advanced the required distance, another toppo way would be formed and so on until the planned number of toppos had been formed. As soon as the road had driven on by and there was enough space to work in, work in the toppo could begin. The toppo way was 6 feet square, much smaller than the road, being made just large enough to work in and remove the coal. Unlike the main road it would serve no useful purpose after the coal was worked out. When the first 4 yards of the toppo had been blown out, a further area of the floor was removed to make a small runway to accommodate the trams so that they could be brought in off the main road on a pair of short rails. A flat sheet of steel plate, the length and width of a tram, was then laid between the rails in the main road and directly in front of the toppo entrance, known as a 'stricking plate'. Each tram had a three-link coupling at the front and when the tram was loaded, by grasping the coupling with one hand and pushing the tram round sharply with the other as soon as the front wheels reached the far rail of the main tramroad, the tram wheels came into alignment with the main rails. This apparently complicated manoeuvre became quite easy with a little practice.

When this toppo run was completed, the toppo floor was now 3 or 4 feet higher than the level of the road, about the height of a tram. The floor of the toppo being rather steep, this would make loading a tram quite difficult so a small platform was made at the end of the toppo by raising the end with two stout cross timbers, filling in behind with rubble and laying across some strong boards. This 6-foot square area was called a standing which made a good shovelling base and helped keep the coal cleaner while loading a tram.

If 8 yards per week could be maintained in the road, it would take little more than a year to complete 20 toppos, by which time many of the earlier ones would almost certainly have been worked out and quite a number of others would be nearing completion, each one finishing at intervals or steps, hence the name long wall stepped face.

If there were large coal reserves behind, the road would probably continue and become a permanent way, almost certainly being enlarged to a 10-foot road and being double-timbered by miners who specialised in this work. If any serious undulations were met in the seam, the floor would be blown up to keep it as level as possible for the trams.

Toppos could be worked by one of two methods, known as the 'putt shoe toppo' and the 'waggon toppo'. The putt shoe method was probably the more popular. Two skilled coal-getters, or breakers as they were often called, and a carting boy were assigned to a toppo as it became available for coal production and were known as a company. They were given a number which was displayed on both sides of each tram of coal they produced so that the weighman on the surface could check each load. Given normal circumstances where coal production took place only on the morning shift, they would be the only ones to work the toppo, but if two coaling shifts were worked, another company of men might be involved. Each coal-getter worked about 12½ yards of ground and was responsible for drilling bore holes and the safety of his area. Any debris resulting from shot-firing was easily stored in the gob. Although coal production was delayed during shot-firing, which took place about three times a week, the miners were paid for each yard of roadway they made, as compensation. One man worked on what was known as the loose end, that is the rib to which the preceding toppo had been worked, while the other worked on the cutting edge which in turn would become the loose end in the next toppo. Wooden timber roof supports, approximately 3 to 4 inches in diameter, were erected in straight rows forming small lanes about 3 feet wide, called putt roads. The carting boy, whose age could be anything between 14 and 21, was issued with a loading shovel, the materials with which to make a guss rope, and a wooden putt. His job was one of great activity for if he was to give an adequate clearance of the coal hewn by his two men, he barely had time to wipe his brow, hauling his putt first to one man, loading it, then hauling it down the toppo to the road, tipping it over on the standing, then dashing back to the other man and so on until he had enough coal to fill a tram, which he then had to load. During the time he had been loading the tram, his two men had hewn quite a considerable amount of coal which meant that he could never catch up. Rarely did he have a moment to relax and quite often at the end of a shift he would be expected to work a little longer to clear up all the coal, as it was considered almost criminal to leave any coal until the next day. Each day his job became a little more arduous as the toppo advanced at the rate of a yard a day, and while this would not appear to make a great deal of difference, it was surprising how the yards quickly mounted up in a few weeks.

On some seams, the toppo gradients were very steep and on some the floor was very hard and shiny. This type of floor was known as 'pan bottom' and very little dust ever accumulated here which made it particularly hard for the carting boy to get a good foothold, especially when hauling his putt up the hill, It also made it very difficult to control it when loaded and descending the toppo, and it was not surprising that many accidents occurred on these steep gradients, for as the putt gained momentum, the carting boy was often overpowered, being forced backwards at great speed down the hill, sometimes being over-run. This was a frightening experience as many could probably testify, especially if his light had been put out in the fray; grappling with a runaway putt in total darkness could be very unpleasant indeed. When such conditions prevailed, a small-link chain was provided which was fastened to a prop in front of the coalface heading in the centre of the toppo and stretched to the bottom; with this the carting boy was able to pull himself up the gradient and he could also use it as a brake when descending with a loaded putt by running the chain through a notch in the headboard and pulling it tight when necessary.

In some mines, where a number of toppos were being worked and were a fairly long distance from the nearest haulage, two carting boys might be employed; one young one and an older, more experienced one. In such a case the younger boy would be employed to haul the coal down the toppo while the older one loaded the tram and ran it out to the siding nearest the main haulage.

The waggon toppo method was one worked by a company consisting of two breakers, one young carting boy and an experienced carter, The toppo was worked in much the same way as the putt shoe toppo except that the floor at the bottom was not blown out to accommodate the tram, and the shovelling platform was situated up near the coalface. The tram in this case was hauled up the toppo to the face which entailed laying a tramroad. The task of the junior boy was to keep the two breakers clear of coal as it was hewn, hauling it out to the toppo-way loading stand with his putt, while the senior carter was responsible for loading the tram and running it out to the siding, commonly called the parting, and returning with the empty. During the initial weeks of working in a new toppo, pushing the tram up the gradient was not too difficult, but if the seam yielded prolifically and the output was high, the task became more arduous as the distance increased. Letting a loaded tram down also became more difficult and dangerous. These problems were quite considerably eased by a very simple, but efficient, primitive method known as the 'running post'. This was simply a chain attached to a stout prop at the top of the gradient. Having coupled himself to a tram by means of his guss and crook, the senior boy could haul himself up by the chain with the junior boy giving what assistance he could from the rear. Similarly, a tram could be let down the toppo by attaching the chain to it and letting it out as necessary. If the gradient was very steep and the load could not be controlled safely, a sprag, about 15 inches long, originally of wood but later of steel, could be inserted into the spokes of the rear wheel, causing it to drag on the rails and act as a brake. Experienced men could throw sprags into the wheels of a passing train of loaded trams. The waggon toppo was not the most popular method and certainly could not be adopted where the seams were very steep, as in the Mendip area.

As each 80-yard toppo was worked out, another road would be constructed and more toppos created, as the coal seam was pursued on towards the surface. To work a toppo beyond 80 yards would have been uneconomical so the coal to be taken out above that point was done by driving up what was known as a 'gug'. Driving a gug up the hill, pursuing the seam, was very similar to driving a level road except that it needed to be built much higher and wider. It would need to be at least 10 feet high to allow for some subsidence over a period of time, and to be about 12 feet wide, the width required to accommodate a double tramroad. A gug would be turned off from a straight main road but not at right angles as were the toppos. Work would begin some 25 yards back from the main road, gradually increasing the width of the curve until a long sweeping bend had been accomplished. This was necessary so that a train of loaded trams could be let down the gug when in full production and the extra space created at the main roadside would serve as a small siding for it. After a double tramroad had been established in the main road and laid in round the sweeping bend, the gug could then be taken up on a straight course. The gug was worked, in the initial stages, in the same way as the waggon toppo. The gug would probably be advanced up to about 100 yards, taking it well beyond the 80 yards of the toppos currently working down below. If it had been planned to develop both sides of the gug, a road on either side would be started, forming a crossroads, but would only be advanced a few yards until the gug was made operational. To do this, all development roads would need to be well established, as well as a level space covering about 12 yards of floor; this was to create enough space to stand up to 6 loaded trams on one side and the same number of empties on the other.

A well-constructed tramroad was now necessary, designed to last over a long time. The gug wheel was also of great importance. It was 4 feet in diameter, spoked, and grooved to take a strong wire rope, with a 4-inch flange attached to its underside. It was housed in a strong metal frame and fitted horizontally into it. Securely erected high up near the roof, this not only permitted the gug to continue, but also brought the ropes more or less in line with the gradient. The gug, known as a self-acting incline, pulled empty trains of trams up the hill as the loaded ones were lowered down. It was managed by an experienced 'gugsman' who was responsible for marshalling the trains and lowering them safely to the bottom. The gug was equipped with the same primitive signalling device as in the pit shaft. As soon as the gug was made operational, no time would be lost in continuing the work in the two lateral roads; unlike the main or arterial roads, which were always in need of maintenance, these roads would never be of any more value once the coal had been worked out, except perhaps for temporary ventilation purposes. The same large steel sheets as on the toppos were used to align loaded trams with the gug tramroad. Once the level tram-loading area had been completed the gug would be driven on up, the spearhead for future developments. Lateral roads would be driven on in, creating many more toppos, ensuring constant coal production and steady employment for the miners.

These then were the inexpensive and basic methods used for extracting coal and transporting it from the topside workings, by means of manpower and the force of gravity. It would be wrong to assume that the daily work in the mine went as smoothly as it would appear; there was always the possibility of a trivial geological fault putting in an appearance, problematical fractures in the roof, a fall of rock or the odd trickle of water. Transport problems also occurred, all too frequently, such as derailments and runaway trains, and there was always the risk of human error, all making the day more arduous, frustrating and dangerous.

Working the descending coal seams, that is the areas of coal which dip away from the pit shaft, was in most respects a reverse of the work carried out on the topside, and was always referred to as deepside working. Toppos still played the main role in coal production but were taken off drift roads, popularly known as 'dipples', or dipping roads, driven down from the main road. Dipples were in fact gugs in reverse, following the same curving formation. The main difference between the gug and the dipple lay in the vast area needed at the top of the dipple to house the winding engine which was needed to pull the loaded trains up the incline. The gug worked by gravity at little expense, whereas the the dipple needed power and a very expensive piece of machinery.

Miners working in a dipple suffered many discomforts, especially if water was present, and in comparison to other work of this nature, conditions were abnormal to say the least for hewing coal, drilling bore holes and erecting roof props. Shovelling downhill, standing on a fairly steep slope, was difficult and very back-breaking, and progress was much slower.

As progress was made, a single tramroad was laid and one tram at a time let down to the dipple head for loading. Originally a hand winding machine was used; known as a 'crab', this was a portable machine consisting of a strong metal frame fitted with a horizontal roller to which a wire rope was attached, and with a winding handle on either side which enabled two men to take part in the winding operation. It may have acquired its name from the fact that it was so low-geared that it was incapable of attaining any significant speed. It was replaced later by a machine powered either by compressed air or by electricity.

It would be almost certain that at some stage during a development of this nature, water would seep in through breaks in the strata. If it did manifest itself during the early stages, it might not have been possible to instal a mechanical pump for some time, in which case the miners would have to resort to a slow and time-consuming hand pump or even to collecting the water in a bucket and loading it into a water tank mounted on a tram chassis.

Lateral roads turning off from a dipple could not be made at right angles, as in a gug, but would be gradually drifted in, forming a gentle bend. Loaded trams could not be run out onto flat sheets, but were pulled out from the siding and over the points by the dipple haulage rope. Turning a lateral road off from a dipple was a complicated and skilled job. The operation entailed the creation of a great deal of space and a lot of careful planning. The roof needed many temporary supports which had to be erected so that they did not interfere with the many permanent ones, which themselves had to be erected at various angles to ensure the safety of the dipple. When the mouth of the road had been completed, the roof secured, and the tramroad laid, the road would revert to the normal 8 feet and toppos created as in the topside seams, working back up through the coal into which the dipple had been driven down. Coal was taken out virtually up to the main road whence the dipple commenced, but stopped short, leaving a pillar of coal intact to prevent subsidence and possible total collapse. Coal on the other side of the dipple was also destined to be taken out but it was unlikely that two lateral roads would be worked opposite each other. Far too much space would need to be created which would put too much stress on the roof supports.

The dipple or incline would become operational as soon as the toppos became productive, the haulage engine driver being responsible for maintaining adequate clearance. A train of empties would be let down at speed, in neutral, the drum being allowed to run free though controlled by a brake. Most engine drivers marked the haulage rope so that they knew when they were approaching a road and at that point they slowed down the train and allowed it to run very gently into the road siding. Two men, called 'dipple hitchers', controlled the trains. Quite early on in the 20th century, the old primitive signalling system had been replaced underground by the wet cell battery, comprising two wires stretched down the whole length of the incline and connected to a bell in the engine house. Electrically-powered engines were probably introduced soon after the First World War and were certainly operating in a number of mines by the early twenties.

Quite often, more than one seam of coal could be worked from a lateral road and brought up the same incline, by branching through solid rock from one to the other, but this could only be done after a reasonable lapse of time, when the strata had been allowed to settle down. In some mines, several of these dipple developments were worked simultaneously, covering very large areas and maintaining a continuous output of coal, providing regular employment for many decades. Inclines were also sometimes branched down through solid rock to reach the lower seams, as opposed to sinking the shaft deeper, but this was expensive and not always a great success.

Erecting timber supports correctly was vital and timbering a road was indeed a very skilled job. A set of timber consisted of two legs and a bar or cross piece which fitted horizontally against the roof. Depending on the nature of the roof, these timber sets were normally spaced out at about 4 to 6 feet apart. Occasionally, a large piece of stone, alien to the normal sandstone, was found in the strata, known as a bell mould. This atrocious phenomenon was not visible until the coal had been removed from underneath it; even then the only indication of it was a circular piece of stone flush with the roof. It was anything from one to three feet in diameter and up to two feet high. It was dangerous to work under, being very prone to slip from the roof unexpectedly, and had to be propped up as soon as it was encountered.

Although gas had always been a serious threat in the Mendip group of mines, the rest of the coalfield had enjoyed immunity and been able to work in gas-free conditions since the birth of the industry. It came as a very severe shock to the mining community, therefore, when an explosion occurred at Camerton Colliery towards the end of the 19th century. While the cause of the explosion was not attributed to the presence of gas, it nevertheless was a cause for great concern, and the investigation which followed took some considerable time. As such an accident was unprecedented in this area of the coalfield there was a great deal of speculation. Before any definite conclusions could be reached, another explosion occurred at the Upper Conygre mine at Timsbury. There was some loss of life on both occasions and each explosion bore similarities, both occurring after shot-firing had taken place. Eventually it was discovered that the explosions were caused by coal dust which probably fell continuously from loaded trams of coal as they passed by on the way to the pit shaft. The theoretical conclusion which was reached indicated that the layers of very fine dust were responsible for generating heat and a certain amount of gas, which was ignited by the flashes from shot-firing. Although the cause of the explosion had apparently been solved, no deterrent had been envisaged. The Timsbury explosion was followed by yet another at the new colliery at Norton Hill in 1908, when 10 miners lost their lives, several of them being young boys, in identical circumstances. As far as I am aware, no other explosion took place in a Somerset mine after this, and some time later a very fine stone dust, fuller's earth, was introduced as a deterrent; it was scattered at frequent intervals on all tramroads, the roadsides and even roof supports.

During the early years of the 20th century, coal production was substantially and progressively increased, the industry obviously reaping the rewards of numerous modernisation programmes, although there were still some areas, particularly mines sunk in rather isolated localities, where transport facilities still left a lot to be desired. The rise in output was also enhanced by two new projects which went into production between 1903 and 1906, one at Dunkerton, one of the more easterly in the coalfield, and the other more centrally situated at Norton Hill. Coincidentally, both

66

mines were more or less redevelopments of previous coalmining activities. By the end of the decade two more mines were being started, one also a redeveloped project in the southerly section of the coalfield known as Moorewood New Colliery, and a new drift mine at Clutton in the north, known as Burchells Colliery.

The first closure casualty of the century was the Tyning mine at Radstock; this mine had been producing coal sporadically for some 70 years and was probably one of the most uneconomical mines in the Radstock group. It had suffered many misfortunes and experienced many difficulties in its lifetime which no doubt made it less competitive. The workforce was for the most part very dissatisfied with the general conditions in the mine and resentful when being continually suspended from work or subjected to short-time working, as frequently happened. It closed in 1908 but the pit shaft remained open for a number of years, serving as a pumping station for the neighbouring colliery of Ludlows.

As new mines came into production, the Greyfield Colliery in the parish of Clutton also became a casualty when it was flooded with water. The mine at the time was one of the best in the Somerset coalfield, having twin shafts which were operated alternately from one winding engine. Its wooden headgear was an interesting feature, giving it a look of antiquity, but it was very well equipped. Two other shafts were features of its complex, one being a furnace shaft used for ventilation while the other served as a pumping station, acting as a sump for the entire workings. A large pumping house was built over this to house a powerful Cornish pump. In its early years, like the majority of other mines, it had experienced transportation difficulties, having to rely mainly on pithead sales for its prosperity, but these were overcome when the railway was extended from Radstock to Bristol in 1873. The colliery company then built its own line from Greyfield to Clutton railway station, following a semi-circular route past Maynard Terrace, crossing the road by a bridge at Greens Brook and on into the siding. Initially, horses were used to haul the railway trucks though the line was so graded that the trucks trickled more or less unaided

down to the siding at Clutton; the horses' main task was hauling the empty trucks back up to the pit. As production increased, an old engine was introduced but it too proved unsuccessful and was replaced by a light railway locomotive. Affectionately known as Daisy, this proved to be a good servant to the colliery and was very popular with both miners and the local populace.

Thirsting for further development, the Greyfield Colliery company embraced the nearby colliery of Mooresland, some 400 yards away, into its workings, but the takeover did little to enhance the efficiency of Greyfield. An incline was driven down in the vicinity of the old brickyard to meet the bottom of the Mooresland mine shaft and was designed to haul coal from the Mooresland workings to the surface, but it proved to be a complicated operation. Coal could be landed with ease but it was some distance to the coal screens and the siding, and too many obstacles lay in the path of the tramroad. The new drift was named The Cuckoo, thought to derive its name from a seam of coal, though many were of the opinion that it was aptly named, being so useless.

The Greyfield mine was very popular, and a substantial, contented workforce travelled daily from neighbouring villages to work there. Much sadness was felt when the mine was overtaken by a serious flood in 1906. I am able to write with enthusiasm and a certain amount of pride about the Greyfield Colliery as it holds so many memories of the past for me; I was born in the house next to the mine where my grandfather, father and all the members of my family were involved, both in management and as miners, for a very long time. Having heard the story of the mine so many times at first hand, it has become a legend for me.

At the time of the disaster, coal was being mined from the top and bottom series of seams but of course in different directions and on different levels. The coal from the top series was being produced from what was known as the Top Coal Hole, in the No 2 shaft, some distance part way up from the pit shaft. The disaster happened one morning towards the end of the summer when about 30 men were engaged in hewing coal from gug workings and were apparently working near the surface; in fact some miners said, possibly exaggerating, that they could see the roots of trees. Suddenly water broke in with a terrific force, taking everything moveable with it. As all the men made there way to the pit shaft, they were pushed and buffeted by what had become a raging torrent; there was no time to dress or collect belongings, and by the time they reached the shaft they were lucky if they were still wearing their trousers. Here they hung tenaciously to anything which the water could not wash away while they waited to be rescued. By this time, not many had a light as their candles had been extinguished or lost, and the darkness only added to their ordeal. Meanwhile, water was cascading down the shaft and the lives of men on the lower level, estimated to be about 200, were seriously in jeopardy. Deputies and others waded through very deep water to warn men working in isolated places, and an eyewitness described the comradeship of these men as unbelievable. One deputy made his way, waist deep in water, quite a long distance with his candle cupped in his hand, and discovered two men at the top of a gug clinging desperately to the gug wheel close to the roof. Replying to the deputy's inquiry, they replied that 'we thought we would be safe up here'. The deputy's answer cannot be recorded here, pointing out that even if the water had not risen that high, had the water risen to the roof of the road below them, their air supply would have been cut off and they would have suffocated. There can be no doubt that the majority of the miners were in an extremely nervous state while they waited to be lifted to the surface, but there was no panic, and the rescue operations were carried out so efficiently that not one life was lost; in view of the enormity of the disaster this was indeed a miraculous achievement. As the last cage was signalled away from the bottom, the two pit hitchers or on setters were working in water well above their waistline, and even then were discussing the possibilities of rescuing the nearby pit ponies. Unfortunately they found it impossible and the horses were left to their fate. Both these men were highly commended for their bravery and devotion to duty.

The disaster caused a great deal of hardship to the miners and their families when it was announced that all work at the mine was to be suspended, and there was much speculation that the mine would never be reopened. It took some considerable time to pump out the flood water and as soon as it was possible, a small party of miners was lowered into the mine to assess the damage. Needless to say, they found a scene of complete desolation; huge quantities of sludge and clay barred their way, roof timbers had been washed out and there were numerous falls of rock. It was obvious at first sight that the Top Coal Hole would never be worked again. It was nearly two years before the mine workings could be restored to any semblance of order and even then only the least affected areas were workable. An incline to the deepside, which before the flood had been working the New Vein seam, was reopened and an area of coal worked from either side. Sadly the workforce had been greatly reduced and the reopening of the mine proved to be only a temporary reprieve. After two years of work it became obvious that the end of the mine was in sight and it was finally closed in 1911. Because the headgear and railway remained for a very long time, many thought that the mine might one day be reopened, but it never was. The surface waste tip on the western side of the mine burnt for a long time after closure, and quite often, at first light on a summer's morning, palls of smoke hung over the silent pulley wheels, presenting a ghostly scene. After the flooding, the Greyfield Colliery company, visualising that there was little hope of saving the mine, drew up plans for another project at Lower Clutton, just over a mile away. This was possibly with a view to retrieving the coal in the area, but more importantly, probably to ensure the employment of the Clutton miners. Fortunately, this company, unlike so many others, had the interests of their employees at heart.

One year later another mine had fallen by the wayside, again in the Radstock area. The Huish mine, sunk on the southern fringe of the coalmining town, was producing coal in the early years of the 19th century. Although only a small concern, it survived 80 years of fierce competition with its larger and more popular neighbours. It was not one of the greatest of employers, its workforce always being kept to the minimum.

As mines were closed so others took their place, and at Tunley, on the eastern boundary of the coalfield, a new mine was being sunk, the Priston Colliery. At the northernmost point, a similar project was brought into operation at Pensford, the Broad Oak Colliery. However, by the end of 1915, another mine in the south was closing, Edford Colliery. This had started production about 1865 and did not enjoy great prosperity. It was a very enterprising project, producing some of the best coking coals in Somerset, and specialising in many byproducts.

Coalmining was taking place in many small hamlets in the parish of Timsbury as early as the middle of the 18th century, but the inhabitants of the village will be more acquainted with the two mines which survived into the 20th century, known as the Upper and Lower Conygre pits. Upper Conygre started life at the dawn of the 19th century as a very small concern. The small shaft, haulage engine and boiler system were housed under the roof of a building about the size of four country cottages; the shaft in which a three-tier cage was operated, was situated at the western end of the building, the cage being operated by a small steam winding engine, winding the rope over a single pulley wheel which was fitted just above the ridge of the building. A unique feature of the complex was the chimney stack which was built with white stone and very ornately designed at the top, similar to that of a castle keep. The mine at this time was known as Old Corner Pit. As far as I am aware, there was ever only one shaft in the complex and it has always been a conjecture how the mine was ventilated in its early years. The shaft was surely not wide enough to be divided for the purpose of a return air vent. At the time, at a point just north-east and only a short distance away on the fringe of the village, another mining project was taking place, known as Lammas Field. This small mine was sunk on the western side of the Clandown fault which at this point either joins up with the Farmborough fault or phases itself out. Because of the geological disturbances, no coal could be worked to the east, but some good coal was worked on the westerly side of the shaft, which might suggest that initially Upper Conygre developments might have been connected to it underground; there is no proof of this, but I am inclined to believe that they were, though I must admit it is pure speculation.

The coal seams worked at Upper Conygre were the same as at Radstock, the Great Vein proving the best. The quality of coals produced at Timsbury was very good, and coal merchants came from far and near, sometimes waiting nearly all day with their teams of horses and 4-wheeled waggons to buy house coal at the pithead. The coal was of a very hard nature and some of the older miners were for ever eager to relate how they spent days benching at the coal face before the coal would drop. They also liked to boast of the huge block of coal weighing over 1½ tons, which was manhandled from the face to the pit bottom and hauled up to the surface intact.

A great deal of disappointment must have been felt by all those concerned in the Timsbury coal company when the Somersetshire Coal Canal was inaugurated and no way could be found for a tramroad to it. A little later, their disappointment probably turned to frustration when the railway was constructed from Frome to Radstock, and a scheme to take it to Timsbury did not materialise. At this time trade on the coal canal was booming and Somerset coals were reaching many large industrial towns far afield. This was no doubt having a damaging effect on pithead sales which may have given the Timsbury coal company a good reason to sink two new shafts just to the north of Radford, within a short distance of the canal. Both shafts were designed to haul coal and the two three-tier cages were operated by one steam-powered winding engine. The mine was hastily developed and an underground road started to connect with the existing Old Corner Pit. This proved costly when a geological fault was encountered, running east to west, most probably a leader fault radiating from the Clandown fault, and it was said there was a considerable downthrow at this point. Eventually a connection was established between the two mines and from then on they worked virtually as one. Coal worked at Old Corner Pit could then be transported underground and hauled up the lower mine in sight of the coal canal. It was probably at this

stage that the the mines were named as Upper and Lower Conygre. The name means a rabbit warren to which the two mines were likened after unification.

When the railway company acquired the coal trade from the ailing canal and built a branch line from Hallatrow to the Camerton Colliery and later to Bath, provisions were now made to accommodate railway waggons. A siding was established at Radford Halt and a railroad laid up the few hundred yards of gradient to the mine where a steam winding engine was installed to pull the railway trucks up alongside the pit shaft, enabling coal to be tipped directly into them as it was raised.

A new era had begun but the men's morale was shattered when eight men lost their lives in an underground explosion, about halfway between the Upper and Lower mines. It was said that the force of the blast was so devastating that it wrecked the cage in the Upper Conygre shaft and blew it part-way up to the surface. A wooden plaque was erected at the spot as a memorial. Some years of prosperity followed, but the mine suffered a similar fate to many others when it was flooded out. The water, it was alleged, came from old and disused workings, possibly Withy Mills, and it is believed that the management of the mine came in for a lot of criticism and were accused of negligence. Apparently it was known that the miners were approaching some old workings and they had been using a long drill, testing in advance for water. On the day of the disaster, the drill was either not available or the drilling had been discontinued, but the miners were allowed to work on regardless of the great danger. There was no loss of life and the mine was evacuated in a very orderly manner, but the enormity of the flooding was not fully realised until it was announced that the mine was to close. The closure of the Lower Conygre mine in 1914 left the Upper mine rather isolated, and it too closed in 1916, ending 150 years of coalmining in the parish of Timsbury.

Coal production had probably reached its peak in about 1912. During the First World War, in order to meet national and military requirements, many mines had been stripped, perhaps unwisely, of the coals which had been most economical to work, and as a result many were becoming uneconomical, especially at a time when men were returning from the forces and expecting to find employment. Some unrest crept into the ranks of the miners as they were laid off or put on short-time working. Approaching the 1920s, several mines were going through a period of economic difficulties and one such was Wellsway, one of the Radstock group. It was situated off the main Wells road on the south-westerly side of the town and went into production during the 1830s.

Unfortunately its progress was marred in November 1839 when four men and eight youths lost their lives in very tragic circumstances. At that time the man riding carriage or cage had not yet been introduced, and the men were lowered and raised by the hooker system. The wide, flat fibre rope was still in use, and when men were being conveyed, a long steel chain was attached to the end of the rope, and the men, wearing a sling round their middle, hooked themselves to the links in the chain. It was recorded that the men presented themselves at the pithead for work in the very early hours of the morning and made ready for their descent. As they stepped from the loading planks and the rope took the strain, the hemp fibres broke, precipitating them headlong down the shaft for some 250 yards. It was alleged that the rope had been partially cut by some unknown person. It was thought at the time that it might have been sabotaged by a disgruntled worker, but many miners believed that the culprit had a personal grudge against someone whom he knew would definitely be riding on the rope at the time.

The mine was later modernised and eventually connected to the company's Ludlows pit by an underground roadway. It was said to be an economy measure, the intention being to haul Wellsway coal to the surface by the Ludlows shaft, but was not received with much enthusiasm by the miners who saw it as a threat to their jobs. The final closure of the mine in 1920 ended in a very bitter dispute.

Obviously the government had exercised strict control over the coal industry during the war and extended it into the post-war years until some sort of stability had been restored to the economy. I cannot say to what extent the

Somerset
Miners' Association.

QUARTERLY

✠ REPORT ✠

AND

BALANCE SHEET

For Quarter ending

June 30th, 1919.

government subsidised the mines during the war, but they did give some reward to the miners by way of special awards and bonuses for their extra efforts. However, when these ended, Somerset miners' wages were well below the national average and a great deal of unrest crept into the miners' ranks in 1921 when they were locked out trying to reach a realistic wage agreement. The outcome of the negotiations was far from satisfactory and unfortunately led to the closure of two more mines.

Burchells, a progeny of the old Greyfield Colliery, was a drift mine situated at North End, Lower Clutton. It was very shallow and the incline from which it was developed ran under the GWR Frome to Bristol line, just north of Clutton station. It was ventilated by two shallow vertical but unproductive shafts and from the start showed no promise of being a very prosperous concern. A seam of coal known as the Rudges was being worked near the outcrop. Indeed the workings were so shallow that the miners were able to set their watches by hearing the trains running overhead. Trains consisting of about 12 tram loads were hauled from the mine by a very slow steam winding engine. Coal production fluctuated so vastly that on some days barely enough coal was raised to keep steam for the winding engine and on several occasions the miners were requested to forego their weekly bag coal allowance, which they willingly did in order to try to preserve the mine. The 1921 lockout strike could not have happened at a more inconvenient time. All the Somerset miners were striving hard to retain the basic wage which they were being paid at the time, and the Burchells miners were torn between their loyalty to the Somerset Miners Association and the fear of unemployment. At one time they were almost willing to work for a reduced wage, having full knowledge that if the mine was left idle for any length of time, it would be very difficult to reopen, but the miners' association was quick to point out that such an action would be against their own interests and the principles of the whole mining community.

Coalmining at Farrington Gurney began late in the 18th century but it was only after the railway came in 1873 that it prospered. The seams in the Farrington series were of a very

79

hard nature and produced some of the best house coal in the country. Although it was flooded on several occasions, it managed to survive, though when the lockout strike began, it was said to be in a very sad state and was closed. After it closed, a small group of miners who had been made unemployed, drew up plans and began a small mining project of their own which as we shall learn later was very successful.

When work was resumed after the lockout, most of the mines were in very poor condition. There was still a great deal of tension between the miners and their employers; in spite of their bitter resentment, disappointments and brave face appearance, the miners were still living in fear of being unemployed. The employers were well aware of this situation and were not slow to take advantage of the miners' adversity. Many miners were possibly lulled into a false sense of security, quite unwittingly, when they were offered tempting piecework rates and bonuses on productivity deals. Of course they needed every penny they could earn but as a result coal production rose substantially during the following four or five years, exceeding demand, and large stocks of coal were built up. In 1926, the coal owners' association made very drastic demands on their employees by asking them to work longer hours and accept a reduction in their wage, this at a time when coal production was high in Somerset, and many mines had stocks of coal in their yards. It must have been fairly obvious to the owners that the miners or their unions were not likely to look on such a request with any great favour. On the contrary, at a time when the mines were prospering, they had a right to expect some appreciation in their living standards and certainly not a reversal.

That year of 1926 holds many bitter and dreadful memories for those who lived through it, when women and children suffered hunger and degradation to fight alongside their menfolk as they went on strike. The days and the weeks dragged on, each day bringing more anguish and more despair, as parents watched with horror their children growing more hungry and their clothing more threadbare by the hour. The parents also suffered the pangs of hunger as they sacrificed their meagre daily bread to ensure that their children survived. In those now distant days, very little help could be expected from the authorities. The board of guardians, who were at that time responsible for the administration of the parish relief funds for the poor, guarded their ratepayers' coffers with the vigour of a soldier on sentry duty, and doled out the odd shilling as if they were giving away their souls. Families of up to 10 children were awarded the sum of 15/- per week which, after paying about 4/- a week rent, left 11/- for food, clothing, heating and household sundries. The miners' association had very few funds and the money available for relief was soon exhausted. After a very short time, young single men received nothing, and but for the vegetables and fruit they were able to grow themselves, many would have been on the point of starvation. Fortunately in those days there was a bakery in most villages which, of course, relied mainly on the miners for their trade, and when the crunch came, they were more than generous with their help. They kept people supplied with bread, with the knowledge that there was no money available, just hoping that one day when the strike was over they would be able to repay them. Some grocers and small shopkeepers also played their part by supplying essential foods for children, despite the fact that they too were suffering from the impact of the strike. Many organisations gave their help very generously but there was never enough to go round and distribution was difficult, especially to the families living in isolated houses and hamlets. The Somerset Miners Distress Fund was launched with an appeal to the public for help, but the months went very slowly by, each one bringing more despair, and it seemed almost inevitable that sooner or later the fighting spirit of some of the men would be broken.

Sadly, a small trickle of miners began to break the strike and returned to work on the colliery owners' new terms of longer hours and a reduced wage. Many owners reopened their pits to encourage more men back, infuriating those miners who were prepared to fight to the bitter end. The drift back to work continued but at that stage the return to work was not such a great threat to the striking miners' cause, as most of the strike breakers were only engaged in cleaning up and maintenance work; coal production, if any, was negligible. As the autumn grew near, in that year of 1926, many men were obviously under a very great strain at the prospects of facing up to a cold and hungry winter, and a little later, when the whole workforce of some mines began to vote for a return to work, it became obvious that the fight for a fair and just wage had been lost. When the last of the striking miners returned to work, they did so with pride, and very much resented working alongside the blacklegging men who had betrayed them, many of whom had been life-long friends.

On the general return to work, it was very noticeable that some discrimination was taking place, as the strike breakers were given job priorities in some mines, which only added to the discontent, but this did not last very long as managements soon discovered that good miners were good for the economy.

The only pit not to reopen was the well-known Dunkerton Colliery whose closure was said not to be due to structural damage. One of the most north-easterly mines in the coalfield, it went into production in 1906. Although its two pit shafts were developed as separate units, and both used for hauling coal, the project was operated as one mine. After its development, the workforce was increased very substantially and it was envisaged that many years of prosperity lay in the future. Sadly the ensuing years brought very little prosperity or contentment, at least not to the miners who often complained that their working conditions and their pay were far from satisfactory; many men complained that they were driven very hard, often having to work in very dangerous situations, resulting in numerous accidents and injuries. I have records of listening to the stories of the older miners, relating how they were induced to use some of the earliest coal-cutting machines. They strongly resented their introduction, claiming that the machines only served to worsen the already bad conditions in which they had to work, quite often without proper protection. In 1908, the Dunkerton carting boys went on strike, claiming that they were being underpaid for every ton of coal they hauled. The strike became a cause for great concern as it erupted into a very violent uprising; there were many angry and violent confrontations between the management and boys before an agreement was eventually reached. Work was resumed but there was never any real contentment in the mine and relations remained very strained. It was most unusual for carting boys to promote a strike and the fact that they did so must indicate how very desperate these young men had become. After the 1926 strike ended, a great deal of surprise was expressed when the mine was not reopened. It was thought by many people at the time that the mine was closed to spite the miners.

Another closure followed Dunkerton, this time in the southern region of the coalfield, at Newbury. The Newbury Colliery was part of a complex mining project which had been in existence for some 200 years. It was linked to the Mackintosh Colliery, started by 1870, by a small tramway, and the two were worked as one. The latter closed in 1919 and although Newbury continued, working conditions were described by some of the men as very unsatisfactory, with too much work done for too little return. The mine was reopened before the 1926 strike officially ended and many of the despairing miners broke strike to return to work, fearing their jobs would be lost. Their loyalty was not reciprocated by the bosses who closed the mine only months after the strike ended.

By the end of 1927 most mines were back to full production, but while coal sales were reasonably good during winter months, the mines were producing more coal than they could readily sell during the summer, and coal was stockpiled in the pit yards. Most of this overproduction was due to the extra working time which had been imposed on the miners at the end of the strike, added to the fact that other national coalfields had been mechanised and were also producing much more coal. They were penetrating the market with cheaper coal, which made the coal sales representatives' efforts increasingly more difficult to sell Somerset coal.

In the summers which followed, nearly all pits were put on short time working; to begin with, it was three days a week, when it was possible to claim three days' unemployment benefit, and although this did not amount to a great deal of money, it was a help. The bitter pill was the four-day week when no benefit could be claimed and miners lost one third of every pay packet, already lower than the national average wage.

This was a very unhappy period for all concerned and most depressing when men came up from the pit only to be confronted with a large notice which simply said: 'There will be no work at this pit tomorrow'. Many of the younger miners, most of whom had at least six years' experience underground, became disenchanted with the hazards of a miner's life, the pittance he earned, and the uncertainty of employment, and joined the armed forces. Miners with large families took a long time to recover from the financial difficulties brought upon them by the strike; some struggled hard to pay off the debts they had incurred, others abandoned the hope of ever being able to pay. Those who were unemployed found their hopes of finding employment made even more remote when news spread that two more mines were to be closed in 1929, the central Clandown and the more northerly Bishop Sutton.

Clandown Colliery was producing coal in the early years of the 19th century and ranked as one of Somerset's greatest. It was one of the deepest mines in the coalfield, being sunk very close to the great fault which ran north to south. Although this provided very adverse conditions in the initial stages of development, it eventually became a good and productive mine, always popular with miners. Its situation on the downs at the edge of Radstock placed it at a disadvantage with the mines down in the Somer valley which was its most important transport outlet, as most of its coal had to be lowered to the valley down a long, steep incline. This was much alleviated after 1853 when a mineral railroad was laid down to the Frome–Radstock railway. Many years of prosperity followed, and despite disagreements and confrontations with its management over the years, the miners remained loyal. By 1926, its workings stretched out far from the pit shaft and it was feared that the pit would not survive a prolonged strike, but it did and was soon producing coal again. After a couple of years it was said that the mine's working boundary had been reached, and there were some transport difficulties underground which added greatly to production costs, and led to its closure shortly after.

Of the several collieries which had been worked over the years at Bishop Sutton, only one survived into the 20th century. Opened in the 1850s, it operated prosperously for 30–40 years until closed by flooding. Many of the older miners believed that there was no reason why the geological problems could not be controlled, that the seams of coal were far better than those in many other mines, and that the mine was not properly supervised. It was later reopened with a much reduced workforce but never restored to its initial standard of prosperity. Its location denied it any reasonable access to railway facilities, but one fascinating mode of transport used, as I well remember, was Lovells traction engines, which operated during and after the First World War. The mine did reopen after the 1926 strike but only on a more or less day-to-day basis and, when it finally closed, very few miners expressed any real regret.

It was about this time that a few companies were contemplating the introduction of some mechanisation into their mines. Somerset colliery companies were renowned for their hesitation in adopting modern mining techniques though it is only fair to say that the miners were also very sceptical and suspicious of any changes lest they might deprive them of their jobs. However, the fact that most other coalfields had long since been mechanised and were cornering the markets with cheaper coals, probably prodded them to introduce a coal conveyor known as the 'shaker'. The introduction of this conveyor meant a complete change from the old Somerset mining techniques, as the long wall stepped coalface which had hitherto been worked by the toppo system was gradually phased out and replaced by the straight long wall face. I hasten to add that this was much to the carting boys' delight.

The difference between the two was that where 10 men worked roughly 100 yards of coal in five separate toppos, the same men would now work side by side on the long straight coalface. The coalface alignment would need to be changed in order to work the conveyor which was designed to convey coal down a gradient. A conveyor face could not be operated in roads where toppo workplaces had already been constructed, but if there was a good reserve of coal in the area, a change could be made by rebuilding the road and driving a gug up the required distance of the coalface. A second road would then be driven at the top of the face to act as a supply route. Planning for the installation of a conveyor was time-consuming and took months rather than weeks to complete. First, the main road was built where the coal would be loaded into trams, this time by blowing out four feet of floor and two of roof. The road would be driven on with all haste so as to be kept well in advance of the conveyor coalface. A gug road would now be started which would serve as the main access to the coalface. This was worked in the same way as the gugs for toppo working except that on the coalface side, which would be the starting point of the conveyor face, about 4 yards of coal would be taken. This would serve to provide space for the roof props to be placed about two feet from the coal seam, then a space of about one yard for the conveyor, then another row of roof supports. The remaining empty space would then be tightly packed with the rubbish and debris which was blown out daily. The gug road would be continued some 3 or 4 yards beyond the designated length of the coalface to allow for another lateral road to be built at the top of the face, parallel to the bottom main road. When this top road had gone in for some 6 to 8 yards, the coalface would be ready for the installation of the conveyor.

The shaker conveyor unit consisted of an electrically-driven motor operating an arm about one yard long which worked with a backward and forward motion, very like a connecting rod on the crankshaft of a car. The engine was placed at the top of the face with the arm in the centre of the track pointing towards the bottom road. Two pointed wooden stakes called 'stilers' were fixed between the floor and the roof to hold the engine in place. If the gradient was rather steep it was also advisable to steady it with a sylvester and chain as an extra precaution. The remainder of the conveyor components consisted of a number of trough-shaped trays or pans, about 9 feet long and 18 inches wide.

The master pan, with an arm attached, was bolted onto the arm of the engine. The other components were known as rockers and cradles. These were made up of a strong iron frame, each with a rocker on either side, and were laid out at intervals on the floor at the points where the pans were bolted together. When the conveyor was put in motion, the pans rocked rhythmically up and down and the coal was shuffled down at each stroke, about one foot at a time, until it reached the end pan at the loading point in the main road where it cascaded into the coal tram already in place. The 10 men hewing coal would be spaced out along the conveyor at about 10-yard intervals.

The main road needed to be a double tramroad for about 16 yards either side of the loading point to allow empty trams to be hauled by and made ready without any disruption to the steady flow of coal. Two or three senior carting boys were in charge of the loading and despatching of trams towards the pit shaft. The siding was periodically moved forward as the coalface progressed and it was imperative that the main roadhead was kept at least 20 yards or more in advance of the face. Any debris produced from shot-firing could be loaded into small dillies, taken out and stored in the waste behind the coalface. lending support to the roof; this work was not done on the coaling shift for obvious reasons.

If the coal seam was not very hard and would yield prolifically with a hand pick, the daily advance would be in the region of 4 feet, in which case the yield for the whole face would probably amount to 100 tons. If the maximum daily output was to be maintained, it was vital that a specific amount should be hewn every day to enable the conveyor to be moved forward regularly. In the event of a breakdown or delay due to disruption on the surface, the miners were expected to work overtime to complete the cut, something they did not savour. During any delay in production, miners were not allowed to leave their place of work and continued to hew coal, piling it up behind them until no more could be done.

Moving the conveyor forward every day into its new track was known as 'flitting' and was carried out by a team of six men, known of course as 'flitters'. This work was normally

carried out on the afternoon shift and was important but arduous work. The conveyor was dismantled and the engine, weighing about half a ton, pulled over inch by inch, followed by each of the iron pans, which were very heavy to handle in such a confined space. As the coalface advanced, the roof of the main road was adequately supported, this work being done on the night shift to prevent any disruption to coal production.

By 1930, several conveyors were operating in Somerset mines and while some miners were sceptical, others were excited by the novelty of working with them and it is only fair to say that they were initially quite successful providing there were no geological interruptions. While the fortunate were gaining experience and enjoying the initial success of modernisation there were the unfortunate few who were experiencing deterioration, both economically and geologically. The first casualty of the few was the popular little mine at Tunley.

This roadside mine had only achieved sizeable coal production towards the end of the First World War. From the start, the geological conditions were not particularly promising as it was precariously close to the great Farmborough and Priston faults, but fortunately there was quite a good reserve of coal to the south and south-east of the shaft. The shaft was good and designed to operate two cages but as far as is known only one was ever installed, the other pit rope being fitted with a water-carrying vehicle to supplement the inadequate pumping facilities. The rectangular iron vehicle was operated the same way as a cage; each time it went down the shaft it was plunged into the sump water and filled; on its return to the surface, a lever was tripped and a door at the bottom end opened automatically, the water cascading down a chute. The operation was synchronised with loading and unloading of the cage. The mine was poorly equipped on the surface during its early years; quite often the steam boilers could not produce sufficient steam to keep the winding engine working to its fullest capacity. The chimney stack consisted of a number of metal tubes bolted together which caused many anxious moments as it swayed in high winds, while the pithead gear was for a long time the subject of much criticism. As the mine developed, it became more prosperous and many changes were made; one of the new features was a prestressed, reinforced concrete headgear, something unique in the Somerset coalfield. In spite of this unfortunate beginning, working conditions undergound were very good, probably better than in many other mines, mining supplies were adequate, and the safety record good. The Great Vein seam was worked extensively at Tunley, and in one small area was about 6 feet thick, having the appearance of one seam of coal above another with a small band of dirt-like shale running through the centre. Working on such a seam as this, after the torture of working on a thinner seam, made men feel like ants in a cave, and it was quite comic trying to erect the large roof supports necessary in such conditions, using stepladders to reach the roof. This thick coal phenomenon, for which there was never any explanation, was I believe experienced in some other Somerset mines. All the coal-producing workplaces underground were doubled; that is to say, as one shift finished, a second would move in, which meant that coal was being produced for 15 hours every working day. This system of working was not greatly appreciated by the workforce as it entailed a lot of very unsocial working hours at the weekend. On Friday, the morning shift started work at 6.00am, went home at 1.30pm, had a few hours sleep, and then returned to work again at 10.00pm the same day; while the afternoon shift went home at 9.30pm and doubled back in on Saturday at 6.00am, finishing at 1.00pm. This system was operated to ensure maximum coal production and six days' pay for every worker, but was not a very satisfactory arrangement, putting a great physical strain on the human frame. Transport of coal was done entirely by road, either taken the odd mile or so to the railway siding at Radford Halt or delivered direct to industrial premises by the company's one and only Sentinel steam waggon. During the height of the mine's prosperity, it was often rumoured that an overhead cable carriage would be built to haul the coal across country to Dunkerton rail siding, but it never materialised. Although miners who had a good knowledge of the potential coal reserves were of the opinion that it could have been worked for several more years, it closed in 1930. Foxcote Colliery was similar to Tunley but had been in existence for much longer. Being on the edge of the coalfield may have given rise to abnormal geological conditions which may be why it was never very successful in its early years. To enhance and promote pithead sales and to assist patrons with transport, coal was hauled along a tramroad to a depot on the Radstock–Trowbridge road; its other outlets to coal markets included a tramroad shared with Lower Writhlington Colliery and finally a connection to the Somerset & Dorset Railway. It must be admitted that it was not by any means one of Somerset's greatest mines and was probably overshadowed by some of the more popular mines in the area, but to those who worked there it was just as important as the rest. Taking its geographical position into account its closure in 1931 may possibly have been justified.

Moorewood Colliery was another casualty. Originally sunk, like many others in the area, in anticipation that the Somerset & Dorset Railway would afford them access to the main line, it was closed in 1876, ostensibly because of flooding, though many people at the time thought it was closed in anger because the branch line had not materialised. It was reopened at the beginning of the First World War and that opportunity was seized to ensure that the mine worked to its fullest capacity. Not surprisingly coal was plundered where output was highest and production costs lowest, while working conditions underground deteriorated. All this led to men later being dismissed, and a much depleted workforce struggled to maintain the mine as an economical project. By the end of the 1920s, the tramway to the railway which had been so vital in 1913, was no longer a viable proposition, and road transport was used again, but the poor quality of the coal combined with the other factors to force closure in 1933.

Middle Pit, to give it its correct designation, though miners always referred to it as Deep Pit, was the second mine to be sunk at Radstock, towards the latter half of the 18th century. It was probably producing coal by the 1780s and was worked for many years as a single unit. With the sinking and early development of the nearby Ludlows mine a few years later, the two were connected by underground roadways and from then on worked in very close cooperation while retaining their separate identities. Middle Pit was temporarily closed at the end of the 19th century and its coal hauled up at Ludlows, the two being worked as one. There were two probable reasons for this; firstly, Middle Pit was badly in need of modernisation and secondly, Ludlows was more conveniently situated near the railway. The shaft was reopened in the early 20th century and some coal hauled there until 1926, after which it was kept open for pumping and emergency purposes until 1933. The tall chimney stood for many years as a monument to one of Radstock's oldest mines, but has now been demolished.

By 1936, only 14 mines remained at work in Somerset, two of which were drift mines whose output could be described as insignificant. Competition in the coal markets had eased quite considerably and some of the more productive mines were enjoying a fairly good run of prosperity. This fact was reflected by the generosity of at least one coal company who at this time had installed pithead baths. The first such baths were introduced by the Pensford and Bromley Collieries and in the main were much appreciated. Of course it was difficult at first to persuade everyone to take advantage of this excellent facility, and the old tradition of going home to a tin bath in privacy by the kitchen fire was hard to break. Incidentally, by this time, some local authorities were beginning to realise the need for improved hygiene in workers' homes and were building houses for rent which included the luxury of a bathroom. But the pithead baths really were a good step forward; no longer was it necessary to wear dirty and sweaty clothing home, as this was kept in heated, private lockers, relieving mothers and housewives of having to dry wet clothes and clean up after bathing. Canteens were also introduced, with the service later extended to the sale of soap and towels at reduced rates, tobacco requisites and packed sandwiches to take underground – a boon to those of us who had to rush off to work in the early hours of the morning, quite often

forgetting to collect our lunch boxes from the kitchen table. It was not until the 1940s, however, that canteens were extended to all mines.

Towards the end of the 1930s, underground coal conveyors were being used in at least seven mines, but while the Somerset miners were enthusing over this revolutionary, new enterprise, it was by now pretty obsolete in most other coalfields.

The declaration of war in 1939 had an immediately felt adverse effect on the Somerset mines. Young miners who had left the mines in the 1920s and 1930s to join the forces, and had since returned, were called back to military service. These were all experienced miners and their absence led to an acute shortage of manpower. Coal output was maintained through 1940 but fell in 1941 and 1942. The Minister for Labour, Ernest Bevin, took emergency steps to combat the ever-increasing shortage of men. He conscripted all able-bodied men with mining experience back into the pits, many of whom were beyond the age of military service or had left the mines many years before the war. Most of these men did not appreciate having to return to the mines but they had no choice. The Minister also introduced a training scheme designed to train men in the art of coalmining. The trainees on this often-ridiculed scheme were known as the Bevin Boys. The scheme might have made some contribution to solving the manpower shortage but was certainly not the answer to it. Although these trainees did their best, it soon became obvious that coalminers were born, not tailor-made. The continuing seriousness of the workforce shortage was reflected in the fact that some effort was made to release certain categories of ex-miners from the military forces, but not in sufficient numbers to make any significant improvement.

Surprisingly, in 1943 another mine in the Mendip group closed. Mells Colliery was one of a number of pits which went into production during the second half of the 19th century, probably inspired by the advent of the Frome–Radstock railway. The history of this mine was that of a long succession of misfortunes, so it would seem, from beginning to end. Its workforce, so it was said, was often aroused into militant mood, precipitated by poor working conditions, low rates of pay, and the shortage of machinery and materials; men who worked there in the 1920s were often critical of the management. Conditions in the mine were so bad that any form of modernisation would have been impossible. The only mechanical aid ever introduced was the pneumatic pick which proved to be most unsuitable and was totally rejected by the men. The fact that the Government authorised the closure of the mine during wartime, when coal was so badly needed, gives some indication that the mine must have been in a very dilapidated state.

Miners' wages did not rise in comparison with the majority of other war workers and Somerset miners were bitterly disappointed when it was known that very young women were being paid more than they were to do menial tasks in factories. After the war, the men who had been conscripted into the mines were impatient when they were not released immediately to return to their former employment, but this was something which could not be done overnight. It took quite some time before men could be released from the forces to return to the mines.

Early in 1946, the newly-formed Labour Government set up a National Board to investigate the state of the coalmining industry. This revealed that the industry had been much neglected and was badly in need of some investment if it was to play its full part in the nation's economy; it recommended that the industry should be taken into public ownership. The state to which the industry had declined was truly realised during the 1946–47 winter when the country found itself in the grip of very severe weather and a shortage of coal, which resulted in rationing in most areas when distribution became too difficult. The Government was quite wrongly blamed for the situation, when in fact it was many years of neglect and poor planning by the privately-owned colliery companies, in their quest for large profits, which had created the crisis. On 1st January 1947, the British coalmining industry was taken into public ownership; it was a joyous occasion and one which all mine workers and their unions welcomed, for they

had been advocating such a move for many years. The National Coal Board did bring the Somerset miners' wages into line with the national level and offered very good incentives for higher productivity.

At the time of nationalisation there were ten deep shaft and two drift mines still at work, and it is fairly safe to say that the Coal Board did not find many bargains when they took possession, for most of them had been run down and were badly in need of large investment. The regional representatives of the NCB were faced with a tremendous task when they were engaged to assess the potential of the Somerset mines. The workings in all the mines were some considerable distance from the pit shafts which meant that all the coal had to be hauled long distances underground which was time-consuming and entailed the use of a number of haulage engines, miles of rope, the maintenance of miles of tramroads and roof supports, plus the cost of maintaining the rolling stock, all of which added up to high production costs. The situation now was that the NCB, who incidentally had taken over not only the working mines but also the entire field of abandoned mines, had money to invest, the nation was badly in need of coal, and the miners needed work. So they ventured forth in an effort to retrieve what was left of the Somerset coalfield. No miracles were achieved in the first year of nationalisation though some reorganisation of the existing amenities took place to good effect, and this together with the determined effort of the miners gave management ample inspiration to plan for the future. After many exhausting inspections and much deliberation, the NCB experts decided that there was a future for the deep shaft pits but disregarded the two drift mines at Charmborough, in Mendip, and Marsh Lane at Farrington Gurney, which were thought to have no worthwhile potential.

The Charmborough mine, just south-east of Kilmersdon, and the most northerly in the Mendip group, was the last coalmining project of any importance to be promoted in the Somerset coalfield. It was producing coal by the late 1930s and was worked very professionally by a small workforce in the initial stages. It encountered various

teething problems and it was some time before any sizeable development had been accomplished. Ironically, it reached peak production just before takeover in 1947, but was closed shortly after. Probably most miners would have agreed that it was only a short-term project.

In the meantime, some of the remaining mines considered to have the most potential were being reorganised and equipped with more efficient machinery. In most cases, the old shaker conveyors were replaced by modern conveyors with rubber belts which could be used on any gradient of coalface, and small portable electric haulage engines were also introduced which were useful for hauling coal waggons up short gradients caused by undulating seams. Ring roof supports were ever increasingly being used to replace the old wooden timbers in the main roads. In inclines, where valuable haulage time could be saved, bigger and faster conveyor belts were introduced onto which several coalface belts could be directed, ensuring that the main conveyor was working to its fullest capacity.

Not only did the creation of better working conditions underground improve productivity but it did much to improve the morale of the miners; after only a year of nationalisation it was higher than at any time during the whole history of the coalmining industry. The working day had been shortened, as had the working week, but Saturday working was still necessary to meet the nation's demand for coal, and was paid overtime to those who wished to work. Holiday payments had also been improved, with all statutory holidays paid, and although one week's holiday with pay had been introduced in 1941 to give war workers a welcome rest, it had now been extended to two weeks annual holiday with pay; this was something the miners had only dreamed of before the war.

With the introduction of more conveyor belts on long wall coalfaces, the coal cutter which had hitherto so often been condemned by the miners was now accepted as a necessity, especially on the harder coal seams. The coal cutter was a very powerful machine designed to undercut a coal seam at floor level, thus ending the very laborious task of benching. The body of the machine was made of tough steel and was

about 4–5 feet long, about 2 feet wide, and 14 inches high; the cutting implement was at the rear and consisted of a steel arm, 4' 6" long and about one foot wide, round which a chain was propelled, fitted with very sharp, giant steel teeth, all pointing outwards. The cutter arm, known as the 'banjo', was about 4 inches high and positioned at floor level, working on a pivot. The machine moved along by its own self-winding drum and a wire rope. Two men were needed to operate the cutter, one working the controls, the other being responsible for erecting the stilers by which the cutter pulled itself along. The cutters were mainly used on horizontal faces but could be used on a gradient if it was not too steep. The length of the long wall coalfaces in Somerset varied but was seldom longer than 120 yards; each face, by law and out of necessity, was bound to have roadways at least 6 feet high on each side, and the cutter would rest in one of these when not in use. To operate the machine, it was first manoeuvred close to the seam with its banjo extended to its full length across the front of the road, so that the body of the machine and the cutting arm were in a straight line; the chain was then started and the teeth made contact with the coal. The operator would now very gradually pivot the arm in a semi-circular manner until it was at right angles to the body of the cutter, by which time it would have embedded itself in the seam to its full length at floor level, and be ready to cut the face. This preliminary process was known as 'jibbing in'. When the cutter had been jibbed in, the stiler man would pull the loop of wire rope to its fullest extent, which was about 20 yards, and place it round a stiler, which was normally of metal, which he then fixed firmly in niches in the floor and the roof. The cutter would then pull itself forward, inch by inch, towards the stiler, at the same time undercutting the coal. The procedure was repeated until the whole face had been cut. The miners always referred to the cutter as the 'Iron Man' and it was easy to see how it got this name. As it slowly cut its way along the coalface, the whine of the motor and the crunching of the coal as the giant teeth grubbed it out tended to give the impression of some prehistoric monster trapped in the coal seam trying to claw its way out. As it progressed, it left a swarf of dusty coal in its wake, but quite a lot was still left in the cut, known as 'gummings'. One big advantage was that it could also be used to cut in the stone floor when the seam was very thin, giving an extra 6 inches or so of height.

When the coaling shift arrived the next day, they always experienced some difficulty in getting into their allotted places. The men who worked in the centre of the face had to wriggle their way some 40 or 50 yards on their stomachs, pushing their tools in front of them; on arrival at their place, they flattened themselves on the floor, on top of the gummings, and shovelled this as best they could to one side until there was room to kneel. After this the conveyor was set in motion and the whole of the face was cleared up. When this was done, each man was responsible for ensuring that his allotted space was made safe to work in before the real day's work began. If, after shovelling out the loose coal, there was no sign that the coal was about to drop, the pick would be used to draw out the remaining gummings. If the coal still did not drop, there were a few other methods which could be applied to induce it. The first was to drive large iron wedges over the top of the seam with a heavy sledgehammer; failing this, a hole might be made with the pick over the coal near the roof, and a roof prop inserted to try and lever it down; as a last resort, the shot-firer would be sent for. When the coal fell to the floor it sometimes fell in one lump (imagine a lump of coal weighing 10 tons!); if this happened it meant a lot of very strenuous work to break it all up, but fortunately it normally broke into several pieces, though even these provoked a lot of aching arms. If it was possible to roll large lumps of coal onto the conveyor, it not only boosted the coal sales, but saved a great deal of shovel work as well.

When all the coal had been stripped to the back of the cut, permanent roof supports were erected and the track prepared for the next cut. On such long mechanised coalfaces, the coal was removed much more quickly and an empty space was created at the rear as a result. To counter the hazard of subsidence, some pits used wooden cogs, reused daily, while others preferred to build what was known as a 'running pack'. The packs were constructed at about 10-yard intervals by building two side walls, three yards apart, then filling in to roof height with debris from the roads and any stone or rubbish incurred by the men working at the coalface. After this a good stone wall was built across the front. About one yard was added to the packs each day and the roof props which had been left behind were knocked out and reused, allowing the strata to settle down gently onto the packs.

During these first two years of nationalisation, then, many improvements were made and plans drawn up which were to determine the future of the Somerset coalfield. Unfortunately, these future plans did not include the drift mine at Marsh Lane, Farrington Gurney which was doomed to be closed.

In 1921, after the lock-out strike had ended which led to the closure of Farrington Gurney pit, a group of miners, rather than suffer the indignities of unemployment, decided to promote a small coalmining project of their own. They were granted permission and work on a drift mine started almost at once in a field near the railway; their efforts were successful to a point and they did in fact produce some coal, but alas, their hard work proved to be in vain when they discovered that their workings were too near to the old pit, and for safety reasons the project was abandoned after two years. But this was not to be the end; these hard-working miners did not give up and sought to be given another chance. They persisted and won permission to promote a similar project at Marsh Lane, just over a mile north-west of the old pit, to work a small area of coal which they knew to be still intact. At this time money was very scarce to say the least, but a co-operative company was formed, each paying equal shares and each sharing the work which began in earnest in the summer of 1924. Obviously, only a small amount of coal was produced during the initial stages of the development, but a little later production improved quite considerably, and the small workforce was increased. What coal was not sold at the pithead was transported to customers by road. The 1926 strike posed a problem for the owner-workers of this little mine, most of whom were or had been very staunch

No. 5 SEAM.

NOTE.—

The distances in all cases refer to the maximum distances allowed There is nothing in the following Rules to prevent any workman from setting additional supports where necessary in the interests of safety or where instructed to do so by an official of the Mine.

FACE SUPPORTS.

(1)   The distances between Holing Props and Sprags shall not exceed 6 feet.

(2)   In respect of Bars (Flats) or Props in the face and at the Roadhead the distances :—

(a)   between each row of props shall not exceed 4 feet.

(b)   between adjacent props in the same row shall not exceed 4 feet.

(c)   between adjacent Bars (Flats) in the same row shall not exceed 4 feet.

(d)   between the front row of props and the face at any part of the face where filling has been completed shall not exceed 3 feet.

(e)   between the front row of props and the temporary props set in advance thereof shall not exceed 3 feet.

Note that an Exemption has been granted which allows for the use of Props and Lids instead of long bars on the coal face, but bars (flats) must be used to support the roof at Roadheads. ~~from the coal to a point at least 12 yards back from the coal.~~

WOOD CHOCKS.

Wood chocks shall be set along the face between the roadside packs at intervals of not exceeding 5 yards and 4 feet between each row of chocks.

Chocks shall be securely built in the form of a square with each side 2 feet in length. No round pieces of wood to be used.

ROADSIDE PACKS.

These packs shall be at least 5 yards in width, built on a natural floor, be well made, packed as tight as possible, and built to the roof.

SUPPORT OF THE ROADWAYS.

The distances between supports on roadways, where required, shall not exceed 6 feet and where bars are used they shall be supported by at least two supports.

SUPPORT OF ROADHEADS.

Where roof is ripped to make the roadways. Bars (Flats) shall be set under the Ripping Lip and the bar immediately under the Ripping Lip shall be set parallel with the face. There shall be at least two supports under each bar.

Where floor is taken up to form the roadway. a bar with at least two supports under same shall be set at the Roadheads and flats shall be erected so that one end is supported on the aforementioned bar and supported on the other end by props set on the natural floor of the Coal Seam.

STEEL ARCHES. Where steel arches are used they must be set on substantial wood foot blocks laid on proper foundations and struts or spreaders must be used between each set of steel arches. Each steel arch shall be effectively lagged with wood packing between the roof and sides and the steel arches.

Where the roof is ripped at the Roadhead, Sprags shall be set to the face and sides of the Ripping at the Roadhead and Bars must be set under the roof exposed by Ripping.

The intervals between supports at the Roadhead shall not exceed 4 feet.

Temporary supports shall be set under the newly exposed roof of any Roof Ripping.

Roadheads of Airways must be supported in the same way as Main Road Roadheads.

TURNING MACHINES IN THE COAL FACE.

If height permits, flats to be used to support the roof whilst turning cutters or moving over conveyor engines, where possible coal cutting machines must be turned at the Roadheads.

WITHDRAWING OF SUPPORTS.

No roof support shall be withdrawn except by using a Sylvester and Chains, no roof support shall be used as an Anchor Prop but a special prop shall be set to serve the purpose. Full use must be made of temporary supports to roof.

members of the mine workers' union and did not wish to detriment their cause, but a stoppage at that time would have been a financial disaster, and although some miners thought they should have struck, if I remember correctly an agreement was amicably reached and the mine continued to work. The mine was worked and managed in a very professional manner and was taken over by the National Coal Board on vesting day in 1947; it continued to work until 1949 when it was closed for technical reasons, the coal board not being prepared to spend money on what they considered a very short-term project. The workforce of about 60 were all offered employment at neighbouring collieries if they wished to continue with their mining careers.

Not all the deep mines taken over by the NCB could expect to be lavishly modernised; the best that some could hope for was some investment to improve the existing amenities. Some had been working for almost 150 years and had probably gone way past their best; one such mine was the one remaining in the village of Camerton which was still working in 1947.

Coalmining activities had taken place at Camerton since the latter end of the 18th century, before the inauguration of the Paulton section of the Somersetshire Coal Canal. The first mine in this village did not meet with a great deal of success; it was bounded on all sides by very steep hills, and in the early years coal hauliers were very reluctant to subject their valuable horses to the rigours of the strenuous pull up those hills, especially in winter when the very poor roads were at their worst. The coal canal literally passed by on its doorstep and gave very substantial relief to its transportation problem, but situated as it was in a notorious frost hollow, it too was sometimes unreliable in very severe weather in winter when it became frozen over, quite often for weeks on end. Nevertheless it did bring prosperity, and it was probably that newly-found prosperity which inspired the company to sink a more efficient shaft, half a mile further east, in the early years of the 19th century; this mine became known as Camerton New Pit. The new pit was very quickly developed and the two pits were joined by an underground roadway, though they each retained their

108

separate identities until the dawn of the 20th century when the older mine ceased its coal production; it was kept open as a safety return and ventilation shaft but it was later closed after these problems had been solved. Access to the New Pit was no better, in fact it was probably worse, but in an effort to promote their pithead sales, a coal wharf was established at Red Hill, Meadgate, where trams of coal were hauled up a tramroad by a steam winding engine. The end of the 19th century saw the closing of the canal and the advent of the railway when a branch line was constructed from Hallatrow station to Camerton New Pit; this line was later extended to Limpley Stoke and eventually carried passengers in addition to the coal trains. Long road journeys were no longer necessary; the railway was able to transport coal much more quickly and efficiently to the heavy industries, which were expanding very rapidly, and pithead sales were reduced more or less to local requirements and miners' free coal issues, though the old coal wharf remained operational almost to the end. For many years Camerton Colliery experienced a mixture of prosperity and misfortunes, its best probably being those of the early 20th century when a fairly large workforce was employed at the mine, coming from many of the surrounding villages.

After over 100 years of continuous working, obviously the coalfaces were very distant from the pit shaft; this entailed the use of numerous haulage engines which could not be speeded up and whose journeys were very time-consuming; add to this the cost of maintenance of roads, rolling stock and working materials, and it becomes evident how the cost of production was affected; some idea of how far the workings were from the pit shaft may be realised by the fact that the mine had an underground linkage to the Braysdown Colliery workings, somewhere in the Peasedown area. At the time of nationalisation, it was the opinion of the NCB that the mine was badly run down, and inefficient beyond any financial help; its closure seemed imminent, but some reorganisation was carried out underground which it was hoped would improve its economy; after two years, however, it was said that no worthwhile improvement had been made and its closure was once again being considered. At this point, the miners and their union leaders protested very vigorously to the NCB in an effort to save the mine; they claimed that the coal seams and reserves were good for many years to come and that the mine could still be worked successfully, and after much consultation, it was given another chance. Work continued until 1950 at the end of which it was said that the desired improvements had not been achieved; the final decision was made, and it was closed. The closing of Camerton was a great disappointment to the miners, some of whom had worked there most of their working lives. It was quite possible that a great deal of coal still remained in the area, and for a man working at the coalface on a good seam of coal to be told that it was no longer economic to work it, was something beyond his comprehension, and it was very difficult to convince him that it was too costly to produce. The NCB came in for a great deal of criticism from the Camerton miners at the time and it was most ironic that they were being so critical of their management while other miners were so full of praise for their very favourable achievements in other mines. While some preferred to take redundancy, most of the Camerton miners were transferred to other mines with as little inconvenience as was possible, transport being provided. Guaranteed and subsidised transport to and from their places of work was one redeeming feature introduced by the coal board which the miners very much appreciated; many mining villages, where mines had been closed, were anything up to 10 miles away from the nearest mine, and men as far afield as Bristol were being transported to the coalfield daily.

Coal was still in great demand at this time, mainly from power stations in the area which were working at full capacity in an effort to meet the ever increasing demands of industrial and domestic users, and it might be interesting to note that as late as 1950 there were still quite a lot of people living in rural areas who were not supplied with electricity.

After the closure of Camerton, there were nine deep coalmines remaining, and it was becoming increasingly difficult in some of these mines to locate areas of coal which could be worked successfully and economically; some were already reduced to working odd pockets of coal which had been discarded many years before, and any one of them could have expected to be the next one to come under consideration for closure. These were very trying times for both management and men, and there were occasions when relations between them became very strained, particularly when the miners were asked to work harder on unrewarding tasks, preparing for coal production, with no extra pay, in an effort to keep the mines working.

After just short of 200 years of continuous coalmining in Radstock, most miners would probably agree that the bulk of the coal reserves in the area had been exhausted, and this was borne out by the fact that only Ludlows mine was still working at the time of nationalisation, after a very remarkable run of some 157 years, and it probably came as no surprise when its economic stability was being investigated. The Ludlows coalmine might be described as the king-pin or hub of coalmining at Radstock, and at some stage had raised coal from Middle Pit and Wellsway Collieries. With the closing of Tynings, Wellsway and Middle Pit earlier in the century, its centralised locality provided it with the unique opportunity to work out the remaining coal reserves in the Radstock area, which probably accounted for its very long life. During the initial stages of its development, in the late years of the 18th and very early years of the 19th centuries, the hilly contours of land surrounding the mine posed many transport problems, but its fortune was soon to change with the inauguration of the Somersetshire Coal Canal tramroad, when it was able to expand its coal trade into a much wider market, and it was again blessed with more good fortune when the railway from Frome passed by on its doorstep in 1853. This mine, so it was said, was very backward for many years, and was probably the last of the Radstock group to be modernised, but in spite of this it was very popular and provided employment for many thousands of miners. Of course it had its troubles from time to time, and was quite often the scene of many bitter disputes between management and men when irregularities in pay and conditions occurred. To what extent the mine had been mechanised before

111

nationalisation I cannot say, but the NCB did inject some capital into its economy, and many improvements were made, though it was most unlikely that any long-term plans were envisaged, and it was probably fairly obvious to all concerned that its coal reserves were nearing exhaustion. When Ludlows closed in 1954, a long chapter of industrial history closed with it, and for many years it was difficult to imagine this thriving country town without a coalmine. It is most unlikely that there will ever be an industry at Radstock to equal the importance of coalmining, but the community will always have the consolation of knowing that it did much to enhance its environment.

During 1953 and 1954, the NCB had probably drawn up its long-term plans for what was left of the coalfield, and had designated the mines which had the best potential coal reserves and were worthy of further investment. After the closure of Ludlows, just eight working mines remained, several of which might have been regarded as unsuitable for any further investment, but might still be worked for several years at a minimum economic level. Meanwhile, another enterprising project was in its initial stages; it involved the re-opening of an old pit shaft known as the Strap, located in the Mendip coalfield, in the Stratton-on-the-Fosse and Nettlebridge area. This project, if successful, would eventually be incorporated into the New Rock Colliery, which was to be redeveloped and reorganised, some half mile or so away. Experiments with modern coal-cutting machines and self-loading conveyors were also being carried out before being installed in those mines where they could be best employed. The final preparatory plan for the reorganisation of the coalfield was a very responsible undertaking and was carried out in a very precise manner. Unfortunately, as history will reveal, the number of mines was to be whittled down in rather quick succession, as several popular mines were closed.

The Bromley coal mine, one of the most northerly in Somerset, was situated in the Stanton Drew area, just off the main Bath to Weston-super-Mare road. It was sunk during the 1870s and was very slow to develop. If it was true what the old miners used to tell us, it only became a coalmine by

112

pure chance; they claimed it was only intended as a water well for watering cattle, and judging by the size of the pit shaft this could well be true, for it was probably the smallest in Somerset. Surely, had it been intended as a coalmine, it would have been very much larger. A small, three-tier cage was operated in this tiny shaft, each tier holding one small tram of coal; these trams were probably the smallest ever to be used during the era of modern coalmining, and when fully loaded, contained about only seven cwt of coal, but there was a great advantage to using these small trams in that they were very easy to handle in confined spaces underground. An old steam pump was housed part way up the shaft in a recess, possibly an old coal-hole where a seam of coal had previously been worked in earlier years, and when riding the shaft in the cage, it was not uncommon to get a burst of hot steam in the back of one's neck from the exhaust. Some coal had been worked on other seams in earlier years, but at the beginning of the 20th century the bulk of its production was being obtained from the Nos 4 and 5 seams; No 4 seam was about 22 inches thick, and was of a very soft nature; it was fairly easy to hew by hand pick, and therefore very productive, but the coal was rather poor in quality and only suitable for industrial purposes. The roof over this seam was good but pitched down rather quickly; the floor of the seam was soft, and of a clay-like nature which tore up quickly and was quick to turn to dust, which made the carting boys' job much harder when it became deep on the floor. No 5 seam was just the opposite; it was hard in nature, about two feet thick, and was of exceptionally good quality, always in great demand by domestic users; being harder to hew, it did not yield as prolifically as No 4. A band of hard clay over the top of this seam, about four to six inches thick, made a welcome increase in the height in which to work; this was too soft to prop up and had to be ripped down, but the roof above it was good. This clay was very heavy, almost the weight of lead, something probably not seen in any other mine, but the floor of the seam was hard and shiny and very slippery to walk on, a real pan bottom.

By 1910, the topside coal had been exhausted and a main road had been driven in about one mile from the pit shaft,

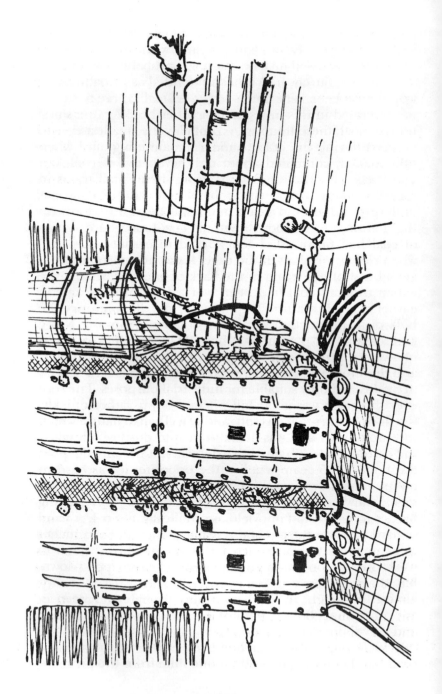

in a westerly direction. Three inclines, or dipples, had been turned off into the deepside; these had been planned to ensure the mine's coal production for some years ahead, and quite a large area of coal was being excavated, heading more or less north-east.

Even at this early stage, electricity was taking over from steam and compressed-air machinery underground, and powerful electric winding engines had been installed at the head of each incline to ensure the maximum haulage efficiency, while pit ponies traversed the main road in relays, hauling long trains of trams along this almost level tramroad to give an adequate clearance. There was very little, if any, geological disturbance in this area, and a good steady coal output was maintained for many years, but approaching the 1930s, the nearest workings were about one mile away from the pit shaft. This meant that much more time was being spent in haulage, and therefore coal production was falling as a result. In the meantime, a branch was being driven south of the shaft to reach a new area of coal, which would be the next production area. This new development proved to be successful, and was to be the subject of an experiment with a coal cutter and a shaker conveyor, on a long wall coal face 80 yards in length. The project itself was an immediate success, but there were days when the small pit shaft could not give an adequate clearance; therefore, the coalface could not be cleared on time, and the miners were required to work overtime on many occasions to maintain the maximum daily cut. The cutter's introduction was the beginning of the end for the notorious guss and crook which had been used by boys to haul coal from the face for some 200 years. For many years, coal was transported from the colliery by road, but after the sinking and development of the Broad Oak colliery at Pensford, a tramroad was constructed from Bromley to Pensford, about a mile or so long, and from that time onwards all coal from Bromley, with the exception of pithead sales, was hauled across to Pensford and loaded directly into railway trucks. The tramroad was operated by a main and tail rope haulage system from a stationary winding engine at Pensford. The two mines were then operating as the Pensford and Bromley Collieries Company. After the installation of the pithead baths at Pensford, which the Bromley miners also used, they were transported to and from Bromley across the tramroad daily in specially-designed miniature railway carriages. When the area of coal on the south side of the shaft was first developed, in 1929, it was estimated that it would add about 40 years to the life of the mine, but at the time of nationalisation the area had been extensively worked, and the use of coal cutters and conveyors had probably exhausted it much more quickly. The workings were once again very distant from the pit shaft, and the workforce had been very substantially reduced, perhaps to some degree because of the labour shortage caused by the war, and it was not likely that NCB had any long term plans for the mine. They did make short-term improvements but by 1957 it was said that the economy of the mine was in a very poor state, and it was closed. Some of the miners were taken on at Pensford, others went to pits of their choice or where they were most needed, while others retired or took redundancy.

The Broad Oak colliery at Pensford was the last deep mine shaft to be sunk in the Somerset coalfield. It was in its sinking stage in 1914, but this was interrupted by the outbreak of the First World War, when the German mining engineers engaged in the work were either sent home or interned, and a team of Somerset miners was engaged to finish the task; it was some time before coal production of any importance commenced. The shaft was the best ever sunk in Somerset, very well constructed and lined with red bricks, and was large enough to operate two cages, each capable of holding two large trams of coal in single decks; it was designed to work a number of coal seams but unfortunately this ambition was not realised when the depth of the shaft had to be curtailed as a huge volume of water was encountered. In the early years, development was confined mainly to the working of Nos 1 and 2 seams, which were not of a very good quality but were fairly productive, but as developments were extended further afield, the geological conditions became less favourable. The development of No 3 seam did not prove very successful;

the roof above it was very bad, and in places was very little better than a bed of burnt cinders which might suggest that some volcanic action might have taken place not too far after the formation of the coal seam, and covered it with burnt lava. When the coal cutter was introduced to it, the experiences of the miners were not very pleasant. There was a great deal of geological disturbance to the north-east of the pit shaft, and on the westerly side the coal seams were very undulating, which played havoc with the already complicated haulage system. During the latter part of the 1930s, an incline had been driven down in an effort to reach Nos 4 and 5 seams which had been worked so successfully at the Bromley Colliery, but once again the attempt was thwarted by copious volumes of water; a large sump was made to contain the water, pumps were installed, and a little later a second incline was driven down, parallel to the first, possibly in hope that the water would be drained off, but there were still many large streamers pouring from the roof and as a last resort it was decided to try using cement. Long bore holes were bored into the breaks in the roof and the sides, and large quantities of liquid cement pumped into them; the breaks were sealed, the water reduced to mere trickles, and another remarkable feat of mining engineering had been achieved.

At the time of nationalisation, the mine was in need of financial investment and some reorganisation; many geological faults were probed, which revealed a continuation of the No 2 seam, but it became very undulating and caused more haulage problems, which were eventually overcome. Quite soon, a number of long wall coal faces were opened up, equipped with conveyor belts, the coal cutter being used on some while others were hewn by hand picks. Although the coal from this seam was only of industrial quality, it did much to restore the economy of the colliery and helped many local industries, some of whom at that time had some difficulty in getting enough coal to meet their requirements. By about 1953 No 2 seam was veering into an area where there was a great deal of geological disturbance, and was not of course much more distant from the pit shaft, adding daily to the haulage problems; already trains of trams were being manhandled many times at various junctions where haulages worked in relays to get the coal to the pit shaft. In the meantime, plans and work had been going ahead with the development of Nos 4 and 5 seams; the cementing at the foot of the incline had been a success, and from this point the two-foot thick No 5 seam was not very far away and was the first to be developed. Roads were turned left and right from the incline, and quite soon long wall coal faces and conveyor belts were being established, and coal production began; it looked almost certain that a long and prosperous future was in prospect. Coal was now being extracted near the old Bromley boundary, and great caution was exercised to ensure that the old workings were not breached and a safe barrier left intact. The main roads were driven on with all haste, working three shifts around the clock, and everything was being done by both management and men to make the project a great success. When the main roads had been driven in several hundred yards parallel to the Bromley boundary, the development of the deepside was started; inclines were driven down following the coal seam, and more and longer long wall coalfaces opened up, but the coal was still being hand-hewn, probably because this method produced the best lump coal, which was very popular as a domestic fuel. The two seams could not be worked simultaneously, for safety reasons, and after a lapse of some time, a year at least, a branch was driven from No 5 to No 4 seam, which was developed in much the same way. Normally if No 4 seam was worked before No 5, the coal was very soft and only fit for industrial purposes, but if No 5 was worked first, No 4 became very much harder because, it was said, the roof pressure had been taken off and it became what was known as 'winded'. The result was that it then produced more large lumps of coal which sold more readily. Coalfaces were opened up but owing to the harder nature of the seam, coal cutters were necessary to under-cut it, and it proved to be so hard that it sometimes had to be blown down with explosives.

This, then, was the position in 1954; the development of the two seams had been successfully achieved, normal conditions prevailed, and the mine looked set fair for many good years of prosperity. For quite a while the success continued, but unfortunately it was only short-lived. As advancement was made into the deepside, the quality of the seam deteriorated and it became much thinner; the bank of clay, which hitherto had been over the top of the coal, disappeared and water began to trickle through the roof, making working conditions very unpleasant; these were the symptoms which indicated that the geological conditions which lay ahead might be changing. No 4 seam also deteriorated in the same way, in fact to such an extent that one needed to be something of a contortionist to work it.

At this stage, in the autumn of 1956, only a small area of coal of any consequence was available to work, and it became evident that the workforce would have to be reduced. A meeting between management and men resulted in an agreement that a number of men should leave the mine voluntarily to work in other mines where they were needed, in order to try and prolong the life of the Pensford mine, while the strata was proved. But conditions did not improve, all efforts to keep the mine open failed, and it was closed in 1958. The development of the Bromley seams had raised the hopes of all concerned at Pensford, many years of prosperity had been forecast, and not even the most pessimistic of experts could have expected to see such a remarkable change in the geological conditions as was witnessed here. It came as a very great disappointment to both management and men when the project failed.

The dust had hardly settled at Pensford when doubts were being cast about the future of the Braysdown Colliery. This mine, bordering on the outskirts of Radstock, was sunk about the middle of the 19th century. It was sunk ostensibly to work the coal seams of the upper series, but these seams did not come up to expectations, which was the cause of some concern at the time as to the mine's future. Later the shaft was sunk to a much greater depth to reach the lower seams and even they proved to be a little below normal; this was perhaps not surprising as the mine was near the fringe of the coalfield, where adverse geological conditions might be expected. Braysdown was one of the most easterly of the coalfield, and at that time was probably the deepest shaft in Somerset. In its early years it relied on the old

Somersetshire Coal Canal tramroad for the transportation of its coal and later the Somerset and Dorset Railway as and when it became available. When it was taken over in 1947, it had been working for about 100 years and was probably not being considered for any long term coal production, though the coal board did try to make improvements where it was possible. Coal was still being hand-hewn at this time; coal cutters had been introduced some years before nationalisation and had proved both unsuccessful and unpopular. It was said at the time that very little could be done to improve the very intricate and complex haulage systems, but a plan was conceived to connect the mine by an underground roadway to the neighbouring one of Writhlington, with the intention of transporting the coal from the southern area of Braysdown and raising it to the surface via the Writhlington shaft; this plan was probably implemented but eventually abandoned as not being very satisfactory. Braysdown continued to work on; pit-head baths were installed, and it was thought by many that there was still some future for the mine. Most miners were completely surprised when it was announced that it was to be closed in 1959.

Going into 1960, there were now five coal mines at work in the Somerset coalfield, and these were obviously the mines which the regional coal board had recommended for further investment. Quite surprisingly, two of them were well over 100 years old, an age at which most mines would have been considered far past their best, but it is possible these mines had not been overworked in their earlier years, and it was considered that sufficient coal reserves still remained to justify further investment in them. Meanwhile the redevelopment of the old Strap mine in relation to the New Rock Colliery development was still being pursued, an underground connection had been established between them, and plans were proceeding for the introduction of a complete new mechanisation programme.

Programmes of reorganisation and mechanisation on a very large scale were also being devised at the collieries of Kilmersdon (Haydon), Writhlington, Norton Hill and Old Mills, involving the introduction of mechanical coal-cutting ploughs, with self-loading conveyors and all the accessories which accompanied them such as hydraulic roof supports and retrievable roof support cogs. During these early days of the 1960s, the older members of the mining community were a little apprehensive as to the outcome of all this mechanisation, and there was much speculation as to whether coal ploughs would succeed where the conventional coal cutters had failed. It must also be remembered that there were very few young men working in the mines at this time; many family miners of the 1930s and 1940s had discouraged their young sons from following in their fathers' footsteps into the mines, and those who did so were very reluctant to transfer to other mines; as theirs became redundant, they preferred to seek cleaner and more rewarding employment in other industries which were being promoted in the area. Despite this, the overall opinion of those who wished to continue with their mining careers was of confidence and optimism, and it was envisaged by the managements that the future held at least another 30 years of prosperous coalmining in Somerset.

There was much preliminary work to be carried out when preparing for such a scale of mechanisation; some roads and inclines needed to be straightened, heightened or widened here and there, and tramroads moved from the centre of the roads to the sides to make sufficient space for trunk road conveyors, while electricians toiled with all the installations and cables needed for such an operation. The coalfaces, which were now to be made much longer, were prepared by the more conventional method, mainly by hand pick. The coal ploughs, conveyors and other installations were assembled and fitted at the coalface by experienced engineers. The ploughs were driven by two very powerful mobile motors, electrically-powered, which were stationed at each end of the coalface, in roadways about eight feet high. The height of the coal seam to be cut was normally about two feet, and the cutting implement was fitted at floor level and gauged to cut that amount of coal; the plough, or cutter, was hauled to and fro along the length of the coalface by a very stout steel chain, which was attached to either side, being kept tight against the coal seam by the fact that the motors were kept in a slightly advanced position. To operate the plough, the cutting implement was positioned at one end of the coalface, and at a given signal, the two motors were set in motion; one pulled the plough forward while the other paid out the chain. Once set in motion the plough was pulled the whole length of the coalface, slicing off about four inches of coal from the seam. On reaching the other end, the plough was momentarily brought to a halt; at the same time, the motors at either end were, by the flick of a switch, put in reverse and moved forward by as much as had been cut, and the operation was repeated in the opposite direction. It was only halted for incidents which might occur during the shift, such as poor roof conditions or difficulties with roof supports. The conveyor, which was also electrically-powered, comprised lengths of heavy steel, trough-shaped trays about 8 inches deep and 18 inches wide which were bolted together, end to end; the trays remained stationary on the floor, and the coal was conveyed the length of the face by two chains which ran along the floor, inside and along each side of the trays, to which were attached small iron bars the width of the trays, very much resembling a ladder made with chains and iron steps, laid on the floor; as the chains were pulled along, the iron bars collected the coal and kept it moving to the loading end of the coalface. The conveyor was kept in very close contact with the coal seam and the plough by means of a hydraulic system known as 'pushers'; these were fitted to the side of the conveyor, and took the form of a long arm attachment about four feet long when fully extended. The working sequence from this point, with the whole unit in operation, was that the plough stripped the coal from the seam and as soon as space had been created, the pushers automatically pushed the conveyor close into the coal seam at the same time as the conveyor was taking away the coal. Each time the arm on the pushers became fully extended, the system was switched off and the arm returned to starting point again for a repeat performance; the change could be carried out individually by the men working on the face, as and when necessary, without any interference to the remainder of the unit.

Electric press button emergency signals were also a feature of the conveyor unit, as were the several telephones, fitted at intervals along the side, with which miners could communicate with the machine operators.

The hydraulic roof supports which formed part of the unit were made in several different lengths, from 18 inches to 4 feet, to support roof heights from 2 to 6 feet. To comply with safety regulations it was necessary to have four rows of these props supporting the roof at all times, spaced at about three feet by four feet; about 12 yards of coalface was allotted to each miner, and he was responsible for ensuring that it was properly maintained, and as the coal was cut and conveyed, it was also in his own interest to make frequent observations as to the state of the roof. In addition to the props, some extra support was given by what was known as 'cogs'; these were very strongly made of steel, and when assembled, were of a pyramid shape, being about 18 inches square at the base, tapering to about one foot square at the top, and were about 18 inches high. As these cogs were always positioned at the rear, they bore the brunt of the roof subsidence and to prevent the metal biting into the stone roof, wooden blocks were placed over the top and wedged tightly to the roof; being of a spongy nature and more elastic, they acted as a buffer and gave way when pressured by subsidence, quite often being squeezed flat. To release the cog, a metal tongue which protruded through a slot at the front, was given an upward blow with a long-handled sledgehammer, which sprung the interior mechanism (like springing a trap) and the whole thing just fell to pieces, quite often creating a very loud and frightening bang as the pressure from the roof was released. With four rows of props, and the cogs standing on the back row, the plough at this stage would have ploughed out sufficient coal and created space for another row of props, which of course would be retrieved from the rear and brought forward; first the cogs would be released and brought forward to the second row of props and reassembled; the rear row of props would then be pulled out, one at a time, and taken forward to form a new row. To release the hydraulic props, a crook attached to about six yards of rope was necessary. A miner

would crawl to the rear row of props and place the crook in a loop, which was attached to a valve in the upper section of the prop, and retire to the forward position; then by pulling the rope, the valve released the air and the fluid, and the prop fell to the ground. It was then pulled forward with the hook and the rope still attached, thus minimising the risk of being hurt by falling debris. This sequence was repeated until the rear row of props had all been recovered and reassembled at the front. If the conditions were favourable, the plough and the conveyor moved forward very quickly, and it was quite often difficult to keep pace with the advancement, and while it was considered to be almost criminal to halt coal production, it was equally criminal to take unnecessary risks. In addition to this repetitive work, each man was expected to clean up quite a considerable amount of coal dust which either spilt over the conveyor or filtered through small crevices; this of course was loaded on to the conveyor by hand shovel.

These machines, technically, were very good in reasonable geological conditions, but only too often they moved so quickly that the roof broke down before it was possible to get near enough to support it. There was also some concern about the roof at the rear (the space where the coal and the props had been taken out), known as the waste or the gob; on some seams the roof might hang up for days or even weeks, but all the while it would be gradually bellying down, and perhaps falling in as far as the coal seam, demolishing the roof supports and burying the machinery in its wake; on some others it might break down as the props were retrieved; on the other hand, it might occasionally hold up for a day and crash down *en bloc* the next morning as soon as the rear row of props were withdrawn, sending a very frightening shock wave through the entire length of the coalface, and causing the roof supports to shudder under the strain, very similar to a mini earthquake.

Somerset mines, what still remained of them, had now been fully mechanised, and as a result, were subjected to many new safety regulations. It became unlawful to take naked lights or any inflammable material underground; electric battery lamps were issued to underground workers, and it became a criminal offence to smoke cigarettes or tobacco whilst working underground, and anyone caught doing so was liable to prosecution or dismissal, or both. This enforced law had a very great psychological effect on the vast majority of miners, who had enjoyed the privilege of smoking underground in gas-free pits over the centuries, and many failed to see the wisdom of the exercise, arguing that the vast amount of electricity being used underground presented a greater fire hazard than the naked light.

As the new machinery was set to begin a new era in the coalmining industry, oil was posing a new threat to coal sales, being introduced into some houses and light industries for heating purposes, and at that time it was probably less expensive than coal. Fortunately, local power stations were still reliant on coal, but as coal productivity increased there was short-term stock-piling in some pit yards. Managements were undaunted and insisted that there were many more years of prosperity still to come.

Old Mills Colliery in the parish of Paulton was the last one to be modernised in Somerset, but by April 1962, after months of hard, preliminary and expensive work, the scene was set to go. It was situated about one mile east of the Farrington Gurney mine, just north of the Farrington–Thickets Mead Road. The early development of the mine started in 1867, and took place mainly on the north and north-east side of the shaft. In fact, very little development had taken place when in the early 1870s the company decided to sink another shaft a few hundred yards just to the south-west, where it had direct access to the main road; this mine became known as Springfield and there can be very little doubt as to what inspired them to sink at this spot for it was only a matter of yards from where the newly-constructed railway from Frome and Radstock to Bristol would pass by. As soon as development began at Springfield, the two mines were connected by an underground roadway and although they then virtually became one project, they both retained their separate identities and coal haulage continued in both shafts until about 1940. After this, haulage ceased at the Old Mills shaft and coal production was concentrated at Springfield. This may have been as a result of wartime requirements and the distribution of manpower, but the Old Mills shaft was kept in working order and was used as an emergency and ventilation shaft. The shaft was the better of the two, though very wet, but Springfield was large enough to operate a pair of two-tier cages, running in the old type of wooden guides. The four main seams of coal which were worked there at various intervals were the Farrington top seam or Brights which was about 18 inches high, the Middle and New veins, about 20 to 22 inches high, and the Church Close seam or Bottom Vein, which averaged about 3 feet in height; most of the coal produced from these seams was of a very good quality, the Brights always being in great demand for domestic purposes.

The mine had undoubtedly enjoyed many years of prosperity, but after about 70 years of coal production it was probably past its best and in need of further investment when it was taken over by the coal board who did much to improve its efficiency by the introduction of more coalface and main road conveyor belts, and larger trams; loading points were also established in main roads much nearer the pit shaft, thus minimising tram travelling time and distance. At that time the main production areas consisted of: an area of the Brights seam, quite some distance from the shaft, veering west-north-west; a small development of the New Vein to the north-east; and an area of Bottom Vein being worked in a south-easterly direction from a very long and steep incline, which was also a very long distance from the pit shaft. At this stage it was estimated that the mine would continue for some 30 years. The Brights development was heading towards the disused old Farrington pit boundaries and precautions were being taken to ensure that a good safety barrier remained intact. The best section of coal in this area was on the topside which ran very steeply toward the surface and was of very good quality, but in the deepside workings, the seam became less steep and the quality began to show some deterioration. After the incline had been driven down some 200 yards or so, the coal seam flattened out considerably, was almost level and had reduced to about 14 to 16 inches in height which made working conditions most uncomfortable, though as the coal cutter was being used in this sector it was possible to cut in the floor, giving a little extra height. As the road advanced to the deepside, conditions worsened almost by the yard and the deterioration was causing some concern, for at this stage, when further development was taking place, every ounce of coal was vital if the mine was to survive.

Meanwhile, an area of coal to the north which had not been fully explored, by the Old Mills pit, was being developed, and if successful, was to be fully mechanised; this it was hoped would give the mine a new lease of life. Coal production on the Bottom Vein had by this time ceased and was now too far from the pit bottom to be worked economically; the incline was steep in some parts, was badly in need of repair, and three very powerful electric winding engines, working in relays, could not give an adequate clearance to the coalfaces which were very productive, so sadly they had to be abandoned. The new development began in an incline in which the Middle Vein had previously been worked, and a branch was to be driven through in the solid rock to reach a coal seam which had been partially worked from the Old Mills shaft. When the branch was started, no effort was spared in making it a very efficient and speedy operation; highly-powered boring machines and power loading equipment were installed, and teams of expert machine operators and miners worked seven days a week around the clock; the branch advanced very rapidly, and the speed and efficiency with which this operation was carried out was a great credit to both management and men who were engaged on the project. By early 1962, a seam of coal had been located which in theory was supposed to be the Bottom Vein, and there was a great deal of speculation as to its authenticity; there was some resemblance to it, but the quality and the texture of the coal differed considerably. The area was very quickly developed and coalfaces were prepared in readiness for the installation of coal ploughs, self-loading conveyors and roof supporting accessories; the incline had been repaired, heightened and widened where necessary, and a powerful trunk road conveyor belt, which would eventually convey coal to within yards of the pit shaft, had been installed alongside a tram road supply line. The roads being constructed in the new development were also carried high and wide enough to accommodate both conveyor belts and supply lines. While this work was in progress, the deterioration of the area being worked on the Brights coal was becoming very much worse, and the mine was being run on what one might call a shoe-string budget; such conditions only added to the arduous task of the miners and to the anxiety of the management. When the area was finally abandoned, the coal was barely one foot in height and quite a considerable amount of roof was being ripped down in order to work it; there seemed to be no prospect of any improvement in the geological conditions. It was at about this time that the old steam winding engine was replaced by an electric winder, perhaps optimistically hoping for an increased output. By early spring the newly mechanised development was ready to begin coal production; many of the older miners were rather apprehensive about working with the new machinery, and at first, as one might expect, there were some teething troubles, but these were very quickly overcome and initially the coal ploughs, from a productive point of view, were a great success. Within a very short space of time, daily and weekly coal production figures began to soar, to the extent that all previous records were easily broken. The success continued, and a few years of fairly good prosperity followed, often being punctuated by natural setbacks, such as coalface roof falls, but a little later on, the geological conditions began to deteriorate, and then what had appeared to be many years of good prosperity at the beginning of the development now seemed doomed to failure. The expense of this enterprising project was probably justified, but was no consolation for the disappointment felt by all concerned when the mine was closed in 1966.

Before the closing of Old Mills pit had been properly digested by the mining community, another shock wave was vibrating throughout the area when rumours began spreading that the Norton Hill Colliery was also in danger of being closed. Norton Hill was one of the greatest and most popular mines in the Somerset coalfield. Coalmining first began here during the middle of the 19th century

129

when two shafts were sunk and development began at the first strike of a coal seam; in the initial stages of the development, its chances of success were very encouraging and many years of prosperity were predicted, but in the following years the prediction was disproved when it was confronted with several adverse geological conditions to the south-east of the shaft, casting some doubt on its future. In fact, towards the latter part of the century it was temporarily closed. About the turn of the century, the ownership of the project changed hands, and now being well versed with much knowledge of the geological conditions in the vicinity, the new owners decided to abandon the mine and redevelop the site. The new development started almost at once when two much larger and deeper shafts were sunk a short distance away to the north; during the sinkings, the geological faults which were encountered were now known factors and were dealt with much more easily, and eventually seven coal seams, from 1 to 3 feet thick, were located. In the initial stages of the development, it was said that the coal production did not quite measure up to expectations, but a little later it did improve very considerably. In its early years, in 1908, the mine was overtaken by a very sad disaster, when 10 men lost their lives as a result of the underground explosion already mentioned.

During the years which followed, coal production was maintained at a reasonable level, improving in the 1930s, probably its best years, and it was possibly the biggest coal-producing unit in Somerset, and certainly one of the biggest employers at that time. Coal was still being hewn by hand pick during this period, coal cutters having been tried and rejected by the workforce as being unsuitable for the prevailing conditions. The big demand for coal during World War Two had no doubt resulted in the mine being stretched to its productive limits, but at the end of hostilities and at the time of nationalisation it was still showing some profit; no doubt the coal board regarded it as a mine of great potential when it was favoured by a very substantial investment programme.

If production costs were to be lowered, some method of conveying the coal from the coalface to the pit shaft more efficiently and much more quickly would have to be devised. Locomotives were introduced underground, capable of hauling long trains of trams; mine cars, holding nearly two tons of coal, replaced the 10-cwt trams, and trunk road conveyor belts were installed in main roads and inclines enabling loading points to be established much nearer to the pit shaft. In fact, everything possible was done to ensure the maximum amount of coal being hauled up the shaft at each winding. In addition, some modification was also carried out on the surface even to the extent of fitting hydraulic 'on setters' and an electric winding engine.

This mine had the reputation of being the greatest, and it would appear that the coal board had the intentions of making it even greater. After modernisation, Norton Hill Colliery became the chief topic of conversation amongst the mining community; it was acclaimed as Somerset's model colliery, and great expectations were predicted for the future. Coal ploughs and combine conveyors formed a large part of the modernisation scheme but the miners, like many of those in other pits, were very apprehensive about working with them, especially in poor geological conditions. Every effort was made to make them a success, and for quite some time they proved to be very profitable. Towards the middle of the 1960s, the coal board, having gone to such great expense to modernise the colliery, perhaps quite rightly expected the maximum use should be made of the machinery in order to justify its cost; in order to do this, it was necessary to employ at least two coal-producing shifts in every twenty-four hours, and if this could not be achieved the economy of the mine would be greatly affected. At this point the coal board were complaining that there was a great shortage of manpower which was difficult to understand. It was understandable that young men were no longer interested in a dying industry, but why were skilled miners accepting redundancy pay and leaving the mines in such large numbers instead of accepting work at other collieries? The answer was probably the lack of job security and the dislike of modern machinery being used in worn-out mines. Needless to say, this was causing great concern, for if a reasonable workforce could not be maintained at this stage the future of the mine was in jeopardy. It was most unfortunate that this unhappy situation did not improve and as a result it was said that conditions underground gradually deteriorated and difficulties mounted every day. Every effort was made to keep the mine open but there was no improvement and the decision was made in 1966 to close it. The decision took the mining community by complete surprise, and thus ended another great chapter of coalmining history in Somerset, as the great Norton Hill colliery joined the graveyard of Somerset's dying industry.

It seems like only yesterday when there were some 30 or 40 coal mines flourishing in the Somerset coalfield and thousands of miners working for a meagre living, hoping that one day their sons would inherit an industry which would recognise the value of their labours and the coal they produced, and give them a deservedly better living; their hopes were to some extent realised when the mines were nationalised in 1947, but it came too late; the inefficiency of yesteryear had taken its toll, and year after year the mines sadly disappeared and the skills of the miner were lost in a maze of machinery.

Of the three remaining coalmines in 1966, New Rock, the last in the Mendip area, was the next one under consideration for closure. The New Rock Colliery, just west of Stratton-on-the-Fosse, was probably producing coal by the late 1820s. The two main shafts were very small in diameter and rather oddly, one shaft was deeper than the other, and only one was ever used for hauling coal, operating a small three-tier cage. It was generally known by the coalmining fraternity that the shafts were not sunk sufficiently deep to encompass all the known coal seams; in consequence, some of the best coal could only be reached by driving a long steep incline through solid rock, which was probably just as expensive as it would have been to sink the shafts to a deeper level, in which case the coal could have been conveyed to the pit shaft more quickly and easily, and possibly at less expense. The fact that it survived for 150 years might suggest that coal production was very low for many years, and possibly only a very small workforce was employed there. No doubt it also suffered the consequences of being isolated from the centre of other coalmining activities, especially in winter when coal transportation was at its worst; with the coming of the railways, it was still some distance to the nearest railhead. Like all other mines at the time of nationalisation, it was surveyed by the coal board to assess its coal potential, who concluded that the coal reserves were sufficient to warrant a very substantial investment, but if coal production was to be increased, a larger shaft was necessary in order to haul the coal to the surface much more quickly; it was then that they embarked on a very enterprising project.

The project featured a mine shaft which had been closed for many years, known as the Strap, and it was this shaft which had become the centre of interest because, unlike the older ones, it was much larger in diameter and most suitable for further development. Although the Strap mine had been closed a very long time, it was comparatively new, having only been worked for a very short time. The reasons for its closure were very conflicting at the time; it was said by some people that it was closed in anger because railway facilities had been denied the mining company, while others believed it was closed because they refused to sink a second shaft to comply with mining safety regulations. The pit shaft was capped very professionally, obviously with preservation in mind, which suggested that the company might have contemplated its reopening at some later date. After it had been located and decapped, pumping operations began. It was not known to what extent the mine had been worked, or whether the coal board had any intentions of exploring its workings; the immediate objective was to connect the shaft by means of an underground roadway to New Rock Colliery so that the planned increase of coal production could be hauled to the surface via the Strap pit shaft. After much preliminary hard work, the shaft was descended and found to be in a very good state of preservation; the old mine workings in the vicinity of the shaft were also well preserved, and by 1957 the connecting road between the two mines was well under way. By 1961, coalfaces had been prepared and ploughs and conveyors installed, ready for coal production in

anticipation of some 30 years of prosperity. While all the preparatory installation work was taking place, most of the normal workforce was using the more conventional methods in an effort to maintain a reasonable output in areas which were coming to a close. Initially, the project was a great success and for a couple of years showed much promise, but during the ensuing years there were geological upsets and other difficulties, and once again it was being said that the available manpower was insufficient to work the mine economically.

Here the question of manpower arises again; was this mechanisation programme planned on the assumption that there would be a workforce large enough to work it? The management knew the strength of the New Rock workforce at the time of planning as they did at Norton Hill. These production programmes were very well conceived projects and were no doubt in the best interests of the industry, but it would appear that too much reliance was placed on redundant miners returning to the mines to carry them out. The closing of the New Rock Colliery in 1968 marked the end of coalmining in the Mendip area and in the Manor of Stratton-on-the-Fosse, where it is alleged it all began, some four or five hundred years ago. It was very confusing and most ironic to think that thousands of good miners were once unemployed and living in poverty when there were many mines, while in 1968 there were only three working, and they were closing because of the shortage of miners. It was also ironic that in the 18th and 19th centuries the coal industry was in dire need of better transport facilities to market their product and hailed the coming of the railways as their saviour, but as the mines closed, they too were being dismantled, having outlived their usefulness. Once upon a time the majestic steam engine proudly displayed its supremacy over the old horse-drawn cart and the canal barge, but motor transport has come to supersede them all, to carry coal once again by road but much more quickly.

Coal mining in the Writhlington area began in the very early years of the 19th century, and of the two main mines, only one survived into the 20th century. This was the one known as Lower Writhlington, on the outskirts of Radstock.

It was sunk and was producing coal during the 1830s, since which time it provided employment for many generations of miners, witnessed many changes in the environment and had many changes of fortune. Being sunk rather close to the fringes of the coalfield, it probably worked the top coal seams almost to the outcrop in the very early years of its life. The mine was at work for over 140 years, and probably owed its longevity to the fact that it had the good fortune of having coal reserves to the south of the pit shaft. After nationalisation, rumours were often widespread that the geological conditions at the mine were deteriorating and it was in grave danger of being closed. There might just have been some truth in them at the time but the unstinting investment from the coal board plus the untiring efforts and goodwill of the miners had a remarkable effect on its productivity, and the reserves of coal proved to be much better than had previously been expected. There were rarely ever any sensational items of information in circulation as to what extent the mine was being improved, as there were about some other mines.

A connecting underground roadway to the Haydon Colliery, which I understand had been in existence for many years, had fallen into a very bad state of disrepair; this I believe was fully restored by the coal board. Whether this was part of the improvement scheme and was used for the transportation of coal is a matter of conjecture. During its 143 years, the old mine experienced many changes; in the early years it transported coal on the old canal tramroad, and then some years later on the Wilts and Somerset, which later became part of the Great Western Railway, and finally on the Somerset and Dorset Railway. Towards the end of its life it was said that the quality of the coal had deteriorated considerably, and it was possible that the fringe of the coalfield had been reached when the mine was closed.

The Kilmersdon, or Haydon Colliery, was producing coal in the early 1880s, and proved to be a very enterprising project. It was fortunate that the railway ran past its very doorstep just about the time when the coal industry was beginning to flourish, and it was probably well equipped to take advantage of the upsurge in the demand for more coal,

at a time when competition was very fierce. By the 1920s, it was one of the most modern collieries in Somerset and was the first to introduce the long wall coal face and conveyor into the coalfield in 1928, taking the record from the Pensford and Bromley collieries by a matter of months. It was also one of the first to install pithead baths in the middle of the 1930s. The success of the first conveyor can be measured by the fact that by the outbreak of World War Two, the number had been increased considerably, fortunately at a time when coal was to play a major role in the war effort. At a glance, its geographical location suggested that it had a very large exploratory coalfield to the south, but knowing the unpredictable geological state of the Somerset coalfield, it would be absurd to imagine that there were no disturbances in the area. As nationalisation was being contemplated, the mine was temporarily closed for a few months while repairs were carried out in the main shaft after the masonry work had become very distorted and partially collapsed, probably due to subsidence. After nationalisation, the coal board was quick to realise the full potential of the mine as plans were made for a very substantial investment programme, resulting in a very considerable rise in coal production which continued for many years, and it was quite often quoted as being the only profit-making mine in Somerset. Steam winding at the mine ended about the middle of 1964, as it did in one or two other mines, being replaced by electrically-powered winding motors. Whether these replacements constituted an improvement or not is a matter for conjecture, but it probably saved the furnace workers a great deal of very hard work. After the somewhat surprising closure of Old Mills, Norton Hill and New Rock, there was always a great deal of speculation as to how long Writhlington and Haydon would survive, and in spite of the fact that the miners became involved in a national strike in 1970, the mine still survived, though unfortunately the end was not too far distant.

Before ending this section, I must mention another important group of workers. The smooth running and efficiency of any coalmine depended very largely on its surface workforce, and it would be very unfair to exclude them when articulating on the subject of coalmining. Surface workers were divided into several categories, each in its own capacity being of equal importance. Beginning with the manager, he was entirely responsible for the working and safety of the whole project, most of his work confining him to his office; in consequence, his work underground was more or less limited to making important decisions and periodic spot checks, but he was always very well informed about the conditions in the mine, which he could also shrewdly judge for himself by the amount of coal which was being brought to the surface. His undermanager was responsible for ensuring that all work underground was carried out in a safe and proper manner, that coal production continued unhindered, and for the smooth working of the mine in general. His work took him underground every day, and his staff consisted of overmen and deputy examiners who all worked in close co-operation, and who were in turn also responsible for safety and coal production. All overmen, deputies and examiners were recruited from the ranks of the coalminers and specially trained for their work. The best coalmining managements, in the main, proved to be those with practical coalmining experience.

Perhaps it might be a little unfair to single out any surface worker as being the most important, but if a choice had to be made, I wonder how many miners would be in favour of the winding engine man? His responsibilities were enormous. Every day miners relied on his alertness and good judgement to convey them down the pit shaft at the start of the day's work, and haul them to safety at the end of the shift; just one moment's lack of concentration could have been disastrous, but they were dedicated workers, devoted to their duty, and their record was impeccable. The men handling the coal as it reached the surface also made a valuable contribution to the productivity of the mine; the speed with which they dispatched the coal to the waiting coal trucks and the pithead sales screens was decisive in keeping the underground rolling stock constantly on the move. The blacksmiths were responsible for the sharpening of the many various tools used underground, including many hundreds of pick blades which were blunted by miners every day; they also did iron work repairs to coal trams and a variety of other metal accessories used in the mines. The value of the services of the men who worked the furnaces, shovelling tons of coal each day to generate sufficient steam to meet the needs of all steam-powered machinery, was very often under-estimated, yet theirs was a very arduous and unpleasant task. So too was the task of the men whose job it was to tip the refuse and the waste which came up from underground; the bulk of their work had to be carried out on the evening and night shifts, irrespective of the climatic conditions of winter or summer. The electricians and fitters were of course responsible for the maintenance of all machinery and electrical installations, and their work was divided between working underground and on the surface. The sawyers and the carpenters made their contribution by cutting pit props into approximate lengths or to required specifications for the underground workings, and by making wooden fixtures and doors, which were used for underground ventilation purposes; they also carried out repairs to wooden coal trams which were so very prone to damage underground. To complete the surface workforce, much depended on the office staff, consisting of salesmen, accountants, typists and wage clerks, all of whom were specialists in their own field of work; each participated in no small measure to make coalmining a successful industry.

As has already been mentioned earlier, after the Second World War ended, most of the Somerset coalmines were very run down and badly in need of further investment, and many were in danger of being closed down. Under nationalisation, the National Coal Board did much to enhance the prosperity of the coal industry in Somerset, and no doubt the money invested in the mines prolonged the life of the coal field; equally, the miners responded and worked very hard to make it successful, but time was not on their side. What a different story this might have been if nationalisation had come sooner.

To the men who worked them, all Somerset pits were great, but it must be said that Writhlington and Haydon Collieries earned the distinction to share with the greatest. The closing of these coalmines in 1973 marked the end of centuries of coalmining in Somerset, leaving a wealth of social and geological history in its wake.

The coalfield has been silent for many years now, and how sad it is to think that we will never hear the unique characteristic puffing and chugging of the old steam winding engines, or the discordant chorus of the old pit hooters, whistles and sirens, as they summoned the miners to their daily work; neither will we ever hear again the rhythmic chatter of the buffers on the coal trucks, being shunted one against the other in the sidings, in preparation for the journey to the coalmines. It is also unlikely that we will ever hear again the shrill whistles of the portly steam trains, as they snorted and puffed their way through the level crossings.

In these last few remaining sentences, I would like to pay the highest possible tribute to the coal miners of Somerset; there never was a more hard-working community of men than they. Their lives were always ones of great hardship, but in the midst of their many trials and tribulations, and even in the face of great danger, there was always the element of humour, tenacity and great comradeship. As for their skills, they were second to none in the world; they conquered the unseen depths of the treacherous Somerset coalfield, and excelled themselves in conditions where many other men would have failed.

A. — Break... CLANDOWN COLLIERY.

	Time	Yards	Days	Allowance	Rate	Gross Wage	Payable
Coal	3				1/6	5 9	
Rubbish			6/.			6	
						11 9	
			Percentage			3 8	
DEDUCTIONS—						15 5	
Insurance							15 5
Rent							

CLOSURE OF
SOMERSET COALFIELDS

Last day of
production

28th SEPTEMBER, 1973

RADSTOCK,
28 SEP 73
SOMERSET